An Autumn
Gleaning

An Autumn Gleaning

*Occasional Lectures
and Addresses*

by Sir Henry H. Dale
O.M., G.B.E., F.R.S., M.D., F.R.C.P.

PERGAMON PRESS · LONDON
1954

Published in Great Britain by Pergamon Press Ltd
Maxwell House, Marylebone Road, London N.W.1

Printed at the Pitman Press, Bath

CONTENTS

1 Viruses and Heterogenesis—an old problem in
a new form   1

2 Extracts from Five War-time Presidential Addresses
to the Royal Society, 1941–1945   21

3 The Silver Jubilee of Insulin, 1946   53

4 The Freedom of Science   64

5 Experiment in Medicine   82

6 Science in Education   98

7 Accident and Opportunism in Medical Research   114

8 Medical Research as an Aim in Life   128

9 William Whitla and Queen's University, Belfast   143

10 Thomas Addison: Pioneer of Endocrinology   150

11 Some Personal Memories of Lord Rutherford   165

12 Medicine, Yesterday and To-morrow   183

13 The Mechanism of Anaphylaxis   199

14 Transmission of Effects from Nerve-Endings   212

INTRODUCTION

UNDER some friendly pressure, I took part in the publication, last year, of a volume containing a selection from papers which I had originally published alone or with different colleagues, and which dealt with the results of researches to which I had been an active contributor. That was, accordingly, a book mainly for students and workers in a special field of experimental medicine.

Pergamon Press have now asked me to make and to let them publish a smaller collection of lectures and addresses, in most of which I have dealt with more general themes, usually by special invitation, to commemorate famous men or anniversaries, or to mark other special occasions. I had been apt to think of these as products merely of my occasional truancy, from what I regarded as my proper business of research; but, when I came to consider a selection from them, I found that they did not begin really to accumulate until after 1939, when war-time duties had diverted me from what had been my main industry, and had then left me superannuated as they receded. I began, accordingly, to think of this collection as a late aftermath of weeds; though I took some comfort from the thought that weeds, after all, should show a greater variety and might even have a greater interest, for anybody but a farmer, than the more uniform product of a planned sowing.

Of the items which have thus been chosen for re-publication in this volume, while many deal with certain aspects and claims of natural science in general, or of medical science in particular, only two, then, have any definite relation to the special subjects of my own researches; and these two are the most recent, Nos. 13 and 14. These, indeed, were also lectures given by special invitation, but to audiences with more special interests; and perhaps their reappearance here betrays in me a late nostalgia for the familiar furrows. I thought that, in any case, their inclusion would matter less, since, in a volume presenting its items in order of date, they would naturally come last; so that a reader with more general interests, if he had stayed the course so far, could, at the worst, come to a halt if he should find them too technical.

Of the others, only one, I think, could be regarded as dealing with a special field of scientific research, but in this case not one of my own. That is the first in the volume, and by many years the earliest of the series. Being honoured with an invitation to give, in 1935, the lecture which commemorates one of my scientific heroes, T. H. Huxley, I thought it appropriate to choose a subject which would illustrate the very rapid advance then taking place in a field of knowledge which, though relatively new, made an obvious contact with a fundamental problem of biology, to which Huxley himself had devoted one of his own incomparable addresses, in 1870. The nature of the viruses was not, indeed, a subject on which I could speak with direct authority; but I thought that I might have acquired an even better qualification for presenting it to a more general audience, from the close contacts which I daily enjoyed at that time, with a group of distinguished workers who were actively contributing to its elucidation. Looking at the lecture again after a longish interval, I have been relieved to find—as a result, I am sure, of that privileged association—that I could allow it to go for reprinting today without any material correction. Very large additions, by somebody with an expert's knowledge, would of course have been required to bring it up to date; but I have left it as it was delivered nineteen years ago.

For some years after 1935 I was too busy with my own researches to spare time for lectures not dealing directly with these; but from 1941 onwards I had to give five successive war-time Anniversary Addresses to the Royal Society. One of these was specially concerned with the restricted, war-time commemoration of the Newton Tercentenary in 1942, and another dealt at some length with the history of the accommodation of the Royal and other Scientific Societies, as the basis of a plea for their more adequate housing by the State. Apart from these I have here included only such extracts from the other addresses as may serve mainly to illustrate the development, as the war progressed, of a concern for the restoration to Science of its freedom and its normal functions, with the return of Peace. For these statements I claim no personal initiative, believing that I merely had the opportunity of expressing anxieties and convictions which were then widely prevalent among scientists.

The same might, I think, be said of the Pilgrim Trust Lecture

on the Freedom of Science (No. 5), which I delivered in Philadelphia in the following year. I fear, indeed, that a watchful
reader would readily detect in this lecture—of which even the
subject was chosen by me in response to request—not merely a
general community of sentiment with some of the addresses to
the Royal Society, but even a repetition of turns of phrase and
illustrative examples already used in these. I ought, in fact,
frankly to recognize the occurrence of repetitions of this kind,
in several of the lectures which have here been included, and to
admit that they might fairly be open to criticism. Perhaps,
however, I may be allowed to urge, in mitigation of sentence,
the peculiar difficulty of excluding them from a collection of
lectures with a reasonably wide but, nevertheless, largely common
background of subject and interest—the needs of and the dangers
to science, its place in education, and the importance of its
advancement by research, both generally and in the special
field of medicine—delivered on occasions of different kinds and
to different types of audiences, or even to similar ones at widely
distant centres. I lectured by request, for example, in 1946 in
Cambridge, to an audience presumably containing students
both of science and of history, among others, on the effect of the
experimental method on medicine in the nineteenth century;
and in 1949 I was invited to lecture to the ancient "Royal Medical
Society" of the Edinburgh students, and chose as my subject:
"Medical Research as an Aim in Life." It was quite natural, I
think, in the circumstances, though not intentional, that some
lines of thought and some of the incidents chosen for illustration,
even some quotations of favourite passages from William Harvey,
should have been common to these two lectures.

And there are, of course, instances elsewhere in the series of
the use of a particular phrase in more than one lecture; so that
a turn of expression which might even have been effective in
addressing one audience on one occasion, may assume the
character of a rhetorical flourish, or a slogan, when it recurs in
the same volume, and may acquire a cloying, even a sancti-
monious flavour, which I should not like readers to suspect me
of enjoying. I could not, however, get rid of all such repetitions
without extensive recasting, involving even the fusion of what
were originally separate lectures, addressed to quite different
sets of hearers; and it was a matter of principle with me to avoid

anything of that kind, as inconsistent with the professed nature of this book. When possible I have eliminated repetition by excision, for example, of a whole anecdote from one of two lectures; but, apart from such cutting, a few explanatory or corrective footnotes, and a few trivial changes of word or punctuation, not made in any case to alter the meaning but only to make it clearer, the items in this volume are reproduced as they were delivered and first published, despite all impulses to try to make them better. They are, in fact, records of what I said at different past dates, and not of what I should now like to be credited with saying.

H. H. D.

London, March 1954

ACKNOWLEDGMENTS

The Author and the Publishers would like to express their thanks to those concerned for permission to reprint some of the lectures and addresses which appear in this book, and which were originally published elsewhere.

Particularly, thanks are due to: The Royal Society for the extracts from Presidential Addresses 1941–45. The Editor of the British Medical Journal, in which "Thomas Addison: Pioneer of Endocrinology," "Accident and Opportunism" and "Medicine, Yesterday and To-morrow" first appeared. The Editor of the Cambridge Historical Journal for "Experiments in Medicine." The American Philosophical Society for "The Freedom of Science" from their Proceedings. The Edinburgh Medical Journal for "Medical Research as an Aim in Life." The University of St. Andrews for "Transmission and Effects from Nerve Endings."

VIRUSES
AND HETEROGENESIS*

AN OLD PROBLEM IN A NEW FORM

IT SEEMS proper that a lecture commemorating the life
and the work of Thomas Huxley should find its subject
in some phase of his own activities as an investigator and
a teacher. A wide choice on such lines is offered to those whose
own work and interests lie on the morphological and descriptive
side of biology; for Huxley's original scientific memoirs show
him as largely preoccupied with the forms of living things
and with the record of their dead remains. As the prophet of
the great revolution which biological thought underwent in
his time, and as its chief interpreter to those thinking men who
could not study its evidential basis in detail, he naturally devoted
a large share of his public lectures and addresses to the evidence
from morphological biology for the origin of living forms by
evolution, and for Darwin's theory of the mode of its occurrence.
Yet, though Huxley's technical memoirs give us few signs of
a preference for the experimental approach to the nature and
meaning of life, there is on record his own opinion that his
chosen line of scientific activity would have lain in physiology,
if circumstance had left him free to choose. In his public addresses
we find recurrent evidence of his interest in the functional
phenomena which distinguish the living organism from dead
material, and in the relation of the life process to the protoplasm
which, in a famous lecture, he termed its "physical basis."

In none of his addresses is Huxley's interest in functional
biology more clearly displayed than in his Presidential Address
to the British Association in 1870, to which he gave the title
"Biogenesis and Abiogenesis." This remarkable address affords,
I think, an unsurpassed example of Huxley's wonderful gift
for the presentation of difficult and complex scientific problems
with a vivid and simple clarity. The question with which it deals
—whether living organisms are ever generated spontaneously

---

* Huxley Memorial Lecture, 1935, given at the Imperial College of Science
and Technology.

from lifeless matter, or only by the reproduction of living organisms of the same kind—was a subject of eager controversy and discussion in 1870. The decade then closing had witnessed the great contest between Pouchet and Pasteur, ending definitely in favour of Pasteur, but not so decisively as to carry final conviction with the whole scientific world. Tyndall had then only begun the great series of experiments which were to complete the victory for biogenesis, and Huxley was able to make no more than a preliminary mention of these eventually decisive researches of his friend. Huxley's own mind, however, was already confident of the issue, largely, as he showed in his address, from a consideration of the past history of this controversy, which had recurred at wide intervals in the history of experimental biology, as the improvement of scientific methods, and particularly the development of the microscope, brought successively smaller living beings under observation.

Until the seventeenth century was nearing its end, as Huxley tells us, the spontaneous generation from mud and putrefying matter even of such highly organised creatures as worms, molluscs, insects and fish, was regarded as almost self-evident. Then Francesco Redi made the simple experiment of preventing, by a gauze cover, the access of blow-flies to meat allowed to putrefy in a jar, and demonstrated that maggots were not generated by the decaying meat, but were hatched from eggs laid on the gauze. At the end of the seventeenth century Leeuwenhoek with his marvellous use of powerful simple lenses, had discovered the wealth and variety of simple microscopic organisms appearing in stagnant water or organic infusions. Joblot, as early as 1710, had boiled such infusions and sealed them while hot, and found that the animalcules did not then appear. But when the study of these minute forms of life had been further advanced, with the use of more elaborate microscopes, the controversy about spontaneous generation, which Redi had so simply settled in the case of maggots, was revived in relation to a new order of life. Needham and Buffon, in the middle of the eighteenth century, believed that they had demonstrated the spontaneous origin of animalcules, even in organic infusions rendered lifeless by boiling and sealed from the access of air; and an elaborate series of researches by Spallanzani was required to detect the imperfections of these experiments, and to show that, when contamination by air-borne germs was really excluded, no animalcules appeared. The discussion died down again, but it smouldered on into the nineteenth century, to rise into new and vigorous flame when the further development of the microscope and of other technical methods, and the experimental genius of those who applied them, had made possible the systematic study of yet a lower order of living beings, the bacteria, which Leeuwenhoek had certainly seen already with his simple lenses. And here again the apparent evidence in favour of abiogenesis eventually broke down, as Huxley felt justified in predicting from historical analogy.

This historical section of Huxley's address, with its emphasis on the recurrent character of human experience in this field of inquiry, is abundantly worth study to-day; and those who wish to follow in greater detail the course of experiment and argument during the two centuries from Redi to Pasteur and Tyndall, cannot do better than consult Professor William Bulloch's article on the "History of Bacteriology," in the "System" published some five years ago on behalf of the Medical Research Council. It is to be remembered that in 1870, when Huxley gave this remarkable address, the clear demonstration of the relation between specific bacteria and the infectious diseases of man and the higher animals was yet to come, with the work of Robert Koch, Pasteur and others in the next decade. The idea of a living contagion was, indeed, by no means a new one. From the middle of the seventeenth century onwards there had from time to time been some who supported it, and others who opposed, and even derided it by caricature. In 1870, what was called the "germ theory" of infection was again the subject of heated controversy, with orthodox medicine still in doubt or in opposition. The theory had received a strong impetus from Lister's antiseptic surgery, based on Pasteur's earlier studies on putrefaction, and from Pasteur's own work on the disease of silkworms known as "pébrine." The bacillus of anthrax had even been seen and described; but there was still wanting the clear proof of its causal connexion with the disease, which Koch was to give six years later, providing thereby the first complete identification of a specific bacillus as the cause of a specific infection and inaugurating the revolution in the pathology of infection, which Huxley could only foresee.

Huxley's attitude was characteristically clear and explicit, with regard to the cases of alleged spontaneous generation which had already been subjected to a really critical scrutiny. The results of that scrutiny made it proper, indeed, to look with scepticism on any future claim for the origin of a known and recognised living organism, otherwise than by the reproductive activity of organisms of the same kind; but not to assume that life could never, in any form and under any conditions, originate from lifeless matter. As an item of belief, he would have regarded it as almost certain that, at some stage in the world's history, life had so originated; and he would have found no ground for assuming that the conditions for its new appearance might not somewhere still exist. And, apart from this philosophical admission that abiogenesis in the strict sense, the new origin of life from the non-living, may still occur, Huxley gives more detailed consideration to an intermediate possibility—that of the origin of living organisms or infective principles, not from dead matter, but from living matter of a type entirely different from their own. He traces this conception, again, back to the time of Redi, and of his contemporary, our own great William Harvey, to both of whom it had seemed almost self-evident. A typical case was that of the plant gall, with its included grub, long accepted without question as an example of the new origination of an insect, not indeed from lifeless matter, but from the living tissues of a plant. For this supposed generation by the unlike, Huxley adopted from Milne-Edwards the term Xenogenesis, the word Heterogenesis, which he admits to be the clearly appropriate one, being at the time otherwise preoccupied. So far as I am aware, Xenogenesis has not survived in common scientific use, and I have returned to the use of Heterogenesis, which bears its meaning more obviously in its form, and will hardly now, I think, be misunderstood. Huxley traces again the successive elimination, with increasingly full and critical evidence, of supposed cases of the generation of insects and worms from the tissues of plants and animals, in which they are found living as parasites. We wonder for a moment whether he is again going to extend the analogy to a lower order of parasites, the infective bacteria; and then we remember that some years had yet to pass before that great new chapter of knowledge began to be clearly written. So far as the knowledge of 1870 allowed him to go, Huxley went with a firm and clear conviction. Infectious diseases of insects, such as the *Empusa* infection of flies, and the "muscardine" and "pébrine" which had caused such havoc among silkworms, had been proved to be due to microscopic fungi, not produced from the insect's tissues, but reproducing themselves there after introduction from outside. Strict biogenesis, or "homogenesis," still held the field, so far as this had been fully explored; and Huxley considers the probability that many of the infective diseases afflicting man and the higher animals may yet be found to be similarly due to self-reproducing micro-organisms, then still awaiting discovery. Huxley went far, indeed, in the direction of a prophetic forecast of that rapid advance in the knowledge of bacteria, as self-reproducing causes of infection, which was one of the greatest events, for biology as well as for medicine, of the following three decades, which closed the nineteenth century. It is the more remarkable that he was still careful to retain in his own mind, and to keep open in those of his hearers, the possibility that a process of the kind which he termed Xenogenesis, and which I am referring to as Heterogenesis, might yet be found to be responsible for certain infective or pathological conditions. And it is even astonishing to find him choosing, to illustrate his discussion of this possibility, on the one hand the infective agent of Jennerian vaccination, which we should now call a typical virus, and, on the other hand, the causation of malignant tumours. The choice, though doubtless largely accidental at the time, gives to the modern reader an uncanny sense of prophecy; for it is just in relation to these two types of pathological process, having many points of suggestive similarity—the virus infections and the malignant tumours—that the idea of the heterogenetic production of infective agents has again arisen in our own time. Now, over sixty years after Huxley gave this wonderful address, an idea of this kind is again finding favour with some of the most experienced workers and thinkers in this field of research.

To arrive at the group of problems which form the main subject of my lecture, we must pass rapidly over a whole generation of scientific progress, between Huxley's address in 1870 and a date near the close of the nineteenth century. It was a generation of intense activity and rapid expansion in the knowledge of the parasitic bacteria, fungi and protozoa, and of their significance in relation to infective diseases. The victory seemed to be going, all along the line, to biogenesis in its strictest form. One type of infection after another was traced to a specific, self-propagating micro-organism; and the closer study of the forms and habits of these, and of the conditions favouring or preventing infection by them, provided scope enough for the activities of a whole generation of investigators.

It is of interest to note that the principle of biogenesis, when challenged, as we have seen, at different stages in a history now covering over two and a half centuries, has repeatedly found its support in methods devised for the exclusion of infecting organisms, by the use of screens or filters too fine for them to pass. As attention was directed to smaller and smaller forms of life, a finer filtration became necessary for their exclusion. Thus Redi kept flies away with a gauze; Schröder and Dutsch, in the mid-nineteenth century, were the first to purify air from living germs by passing it through cotton wool; and Chamberland, in Pasteur's laboratory, introduced filters of porous earthenware for rendering a fluid free from bacterial contamination. Such a filter would hold back micro-organisms of the smallest size which the highest powers of the microscope had revealed, down to a diameter of about one-half a micron, i.e. one two-thousandth part of a millimetre. Since no growth of micro-organisms could be observed to occur in a nutrient medium, when it had been passed through such a filter and was then protected from contamination by air-borne particles, it might well have seemed that the lower limit of size of living organisms had been reached. During that period, when the bacterial cause of infection was being identified and cultivated for one disease after another—for anthrax, septicaemia, diphtheria, enteric fever, cholera, tetanus, plague, tuberculosis—it must have been easy to assume that the development of microscopical and cultural methods would soon lead to the recognition of similar agents for all types of infection, including such familiar and highly infectious diseases as smallpox, chicken-pox, measles and mumps, though attempts to find specific bacterial causes for these had hitherto met with no success.

The first, definite, experimental shock to such an assumption came from the study of a disease of plants. In 1892 Ivanovski, working on the mosaic disease which infects tobacco plants, found that the juice from infected leaves could be passed through a bacteria-proof filter and still remain highly infective. In those days of the triumphal progress of bacteriology, this might well have seemed an example of what Huxley, in the 1870 Address, had called the great tragedy of Science—the slaying of a beautiful hypothesis by an ugly fact. Little notice, in fact, was taken of the brief record of these observations until 1899, when Beijerinck published a description of closely similar experiments. The filtered but highly infective juice of the diseased leaves yielded nothing to cultivation, and the microscope revealed nothing in it to suggest the presence of even the smallest micro-organisms. A year earlier, in 1898, Loeffler and Frosch had made a similar observation with regard to an all-too-familiar infectious disease of animals, the dreaded foot-and-mouth disease. Fluid from one of the vesicles characteristic of this infection, after manifold dilution, could be passed through a bacteria-proof filter and yield a highly infective filtrate, in which no kind of bacteria or other micro-organism could be seen by the microscope, or cultivated in nutrient media. But when a small quantity of the fluid was inoculated into a susceptible animal, the infective principle rapidly spread through the system, with an enormous rate of reproduction; just as the agent transmitting the tobacco mosaic disease showed no increase in the filtered leaf-juice, but spread and multiplied with great rapidity on inoculation into a healthy, living plant.

Thus came clearly to notice a new order of infective agents, distinguished by three negative characteristics; they were not visible with the highest powers of the ordinary microscope, they were not retained by filters which stopped the smallest bacteria, and they could not be cultivated in artificial media, though they multiplied with conspicuous rapidity in the presence of living cells which they could infect. Since they could only be defined by this absence of recognisable characters, and could only be detected by the results of their infective action, it was difficult to form any clear idea of their nature. They were termed "filterable" or "ultramicroscopic" viruses. More recently it has become customary to drop the qualifying adjective, and to restrict to these intangible agents the term "virus," which formerly had a much wider application. Beijerinck had referred to the virus producing the tobacco-mosaic as a *"contagium vivum fluidum,"* apparently supposing it to have no cellular organisation—to be, in fact, in a state of solution, and yet to be living, in the sense that it was capable of reproducing itself indefinitely. This conception of Beijerinck, though not logically absurd, was contrary to all biological experience. Certainly we have no evidence elsewhere in Nature of the self-reproduction, or biogenesis, of unorganised matter in a state of solution. And we shall see that the difficulty of conceiving such a combination of characters has produced more recently two schools of opinion: one believing that viruses are extremely small organisms, reproducing themselves by biogenesis, while the other believes them to be devoid of organisation, and invokes a kind of heterogenesis to account for their multiplication. This conception does not, indeed, assume a heterogenesis as crude as that of the generation of an insect or a worm from the tissues of a plant or a mammal. It supposes that an animal or plant cell can become afflicted with a morbid process in which, to its own destruction, it produces the toxic or lethal agent which we call a virus, endowed with infective properties which enable it to induce the same morbid process in other cells, and so to bring about their death and its own reproduction in an endless succession. And I think we may agree with Huxley when, with reference to just such a conception, he writes, " . . . it seems to me that the shadowy boundary between morbid growth and Xenogenesis would be effaced."

The twentieth century dawned with the promise of a rapid unfolding of knowledge concerning this more subtle type of infective agent, which might rival, in interest and in practical importance, that which the latter half of the nineteenth century had witnessed in the case of the visible bacteria. In spite of the diversion of activities caused by the War, the promise remains, and there are signs of its fulfilment. A number of the well-known infectious diseases of man and the higher animals, for which orthodox bacteriology had failed to identify the causal organisms, have now been shown to be due to such filterable, ultramicroscopic agents. The list has grown steadily, and already includes such important and familiar human diseases as smallpox, with cowpox or vaccinia, chicken-pox, measles, mumps, infantile paralysis, lethargic encephalitis, herpes, yellow fever, influenza, and the common cold. Foot-and-mouth disease, rabies, dog distemper, swine fever, cattle plague, louping-ill, psittacosis, fowl plague, fowlpox are some of the virus diseases already recognised in domestic animals; and viruses are responsible for a whole range of plant diseases, which are creating anxious problems for agriculture and horticulture in different parts of the world. There can be no doubt as to their immense practical importance. On the theoretical side, the study of these agents is raising questions of such fundamental biological interest, as that of the lower limit of size compatible with the conception of a living organism.

The observations which had led to the description of viruses as "filterable" and "ultramicroscopic" gave no information as to the size of their living or active units, beyond the fact that it must be below a certain maximum. Even that maximum was often but vaguely fixed by filtration data, obtained with filters made of porous earthenware or diatomaceous earth. Physical determinations of the average porosity of such filters had little value for the purpose; for the size of the largest particles which would escape into the filtrate would be determined, not by the average diameter of the holes in the filter, but by that of the largest holes. In dealing with ordinary bacteria, which would grow in an artificial culture fluid, so that even one organism passing through the filter could be detected by subsequent incubation, it was not difficult to grade such a filter empirically, by showing that it would retain organisms down to a specified size; but the fact that it retained bacteria of, say, half a micron diameter, and let a virus pass readily through its fabric, showed, indeed, that some at least of the virus particles were less than half a micron in diameter, but gave no more exact information. They might be of any size smaller than that. The limit of microscopic visibility could be more sharply defined, though not with such a clear significance as some have supposed. According to a well-known formula due to the late Lord Rayleigh, the limit of accurate resolution, with transmitted light of the average visible wavelength and with the most efficient objective lens-system obtainable, can be fixed, indeed, at about one-fifth of a micron. But, on the one hand, objects much smaller than this, though not resolved as critically sharp images, can be seen as bright points or discs of light with oblique, dark-ground illumination; and objects much larger than this might escape recognition even by ordinary microscopy, in default of some selective stain to render them visible on a bright background. The difficulty, in fact, by either method, at least in the case of certain viruses, was not to see particles smaller than any bacteria in the infective material, but to find any good ground for identifying such particles as the essential, living units of the virus. The identification would, of course, have been comparatively easy, if it had been possible to induce the virus to multiply in an artificial medium, and to observe whether a particular type of visible particles multiplied in proportion to the infective potency; but the third negative character of the viruses—their refusal to multiply in artificial, cell-free media—stood in the way of any such test.

Quite early in the study of viruses, infection by some of them had been found to be associated with the presence, in the infected cells, of relatively large structures, easily visible with comparatively low powers of the microscope. These so-called "inclusion bodies," or "cytoplasmic inclusions," could be obtained free from the cells in which they arose, and separately manipulated by micro-dissection. When first seen they were thought to be protozoa, responsible for the infection. This view becoming soon untenable, opinion tended to swing to the opposite extreme, and to regard the inclusion bodies as mere degeneration products of the protoplasm of the virus-infected cells, not directly representing the virus or an accumulation of it. Yet as early as 1904 to 1906 a number of observations, by Borrel and by Burnet in France, by Lipschütz and by Paschen in Germany, had pointed to the probability that the viruses of several diseases—fowlpox, vaccinia and molluscum contagiosum—consisted of extremely minute coccoid organisms, just on the limits of visibility as separate objects by the highest powers of the microscope when they had been appropriately stained, and, further, that the so-called inclusion bodies consisted of such ultramicro-organisms closely packed together.

Looking back on these observations in the light of present knowledge, it seems curious that they did not arouse more attention. Perhaps the feeling that viruses were intangible and mysterious, had produced a reluctance to believe that any bodies which the microscope could make visible, even though obviously small enough to pass any ordinary bacteria-proof filter, could represent the virus itself; and it must be admitted that there was no direct evidence of their infective nature, but only of their occurrence in large numbers in cells which had become infected. Whatever the reason, the claim of the so-called Borrel-bodies and Paschen-bodies to represent the viruses of fowlpox and vaccinia, respectively, failed to carry any general conviction for about twenty-five years, when observations by other investigators made their significance clear.

A number of factors have contributed to the progress which has been made during the decade now ending, and largely in the latter half of it. Mention may first be made of the direct demonstration given by Goodpasture and Woodruff, in America, of the transmission of the infection of fowlpox by inoculation of a single, isolated cell-inclusion. They also confirmed, with improved methods, the fact that such an inclusion body is composed of the minute bodies described by Borrel, evenly packed in a structureless matrix. Either the coccoid bodies or the matrix might, of course, be responsible for the proven infective action of the whole inclusion body. The presumption, however, would be in favour of the formed elements, looking like tiny organisms. Then we may note another important link in the chain of evidence, provided by Professor Ledingham's demonstration that the minute coccoid bodies, described by Borrel and by Paschen in the lesions of fowlpox and vaccinia, are specifically agglutinated—made to collect into clumps—by relatively high dilutions of serum from an animal rendered immune to the corresponding infection. Further important progress has been made in microscopical methods for rendering the particles of such viruses visible and obtaining sharp, critical images of them, and in the process of differential filtration; both methods giving very much more accurate measurements of their size. The particles of such a virus can be rendered much more readily accessible to direct observation with visible light, by fixing and staining methods which load them heavily with a dye; but such methods can give no more than an approximate indication of the size of the living, unstained particles. By using single wavelengths in the ultra-violet spectrum and an optical system of quartz, Mr. Barnard, at the National Institute, has obtained sharp photographs of the particles characteristic of highly infective material from a number of viruses, in a living, unstained condition, and has thus been able directly to measure the images and to calculate the size of the particles, which have the appearance of very small organisms. Dr. Elford, at the same Institute, took as his starting-point the work of Bechhold on ultra-filtration through membranes formed of collodion gels of different strengths. By the use of appropriate solvent mixtures, and by carefully standard-ising conditions, a series of membranes was produced, of very regular and accurately graded porosities, which enabled com-pletely independent determinations to be made of the sizes of the infective units of a wide range of viruses. With appropriately dense membranes, these filtration measurements can be extended to viruses so finely particulate as to be still far beyond the range of detection by the microscope. Where both methods of measure-ment, however, have been applicable to the same viruses—the direct measurement of the images of the coccoid bodies, obtained by ultra-violet photography, and the determination, by differential filtration and animal test, of the size of the particles actually transmitting the infection—the agreement between the two sets of measurement has been remarkably good. It has been so good, indeed, as to make it necessary to conclude that, if the visible, coccoid bodies are *not* the infective units of the virus, these must be particles of the same size, but for some unknown reason invisible, either by direct observation or by ultra-violet photo-graphy.

Another important recent advance has been concerned with the cultivation of viruses outside the body of the living animal. It remains true that no undoubted virus has been cultivated in a lifeless medium; but a number have now been caused to repro-duce themselves and multiply in artificial cultures of susceptible embryonic cells. The living cells of the chorio-allantoic mem-brane of a developing fowl's egg have provided a favourable soil for the growth of many viruses, including some which do not naturally infect the fowl. A more simple method still, for which Dr. Rivers of the Rockefeller Institute has been largely responsible, uses washed fragments of an early chicken embryo suspended in a simple saline solution, the survival of the embryonic cells affording a sufficient period for the profuse multiplication of many viruses. Among those which have been recently studied by this method I may mention two in particular. The virus of psittacosis, which caused a stir of public anxiety a few years ago through its transmission to man from parrots, which it infects in Nature, is of special interest, in that its infective units, first recognized by Levinthal in Berlin and Bedson in London, are among the largest recognized in any acknowledged virus. They are from a fifth to a third of a micron in diameter, and can be rendered distinctly visible to ordinary microscopy by appropriate staining. Dr. Levinthal, at present continuing his work at the National Institute, has cultivated this virus in the saline suspension of chicken embryo, and has been able to follow the parallel increases, of the abundance of the minute cocci visible by the microscope on the one hand, and of the infective potency of the culture on the other. Such evidence of parallelism between coccoid bodies and virulence has been carried through a long series of sub-cultures. The evidence for the identity of these minute bodies, as the cause of psittacosis, fulfils, indeed, all the classical postulates commonly ascribed to Robert Koch, though really laid down before his time. There is nothing except their small size, and their need of living susceptible cells for propagation, to prevent the recognition of these tiny organisms as bacteria; yet they comply with any definition which can be given to a virus, unless we are prepared to beg the question, by denying that title to any infective agent as soon as it has been rendered microscopically visible. The second virus which I may mention is that of the brain disease of sheep, known to border shepherds as "louping-ill." This also has been cultivated in the chicken-embryo suspension with complete success; but in this case the multiplication of the virus can only be detected by the increase in the infective potency of the medium, and nothing can be demonstrated by the microscope. A determination of the size of its infective units, by selective filtration through membranes, shows why this is the case; for this virus passes through a membrane of such density as to show that the infective particles are only about one fiftieth of a micron in diameter, and therefore far below the limits of resolution by any microscopical system yet available. These two viruses, of psittacosis and louping-ill, are near to the opposite ends of the series as regards the size of their units; but in every other respect they behave as though they belonged to the same type of living things, and we shall see that there are plenty to represent the stages intermediate between them. Before we consider the series as a whole, however, I must make brief mention of two other groups of infective agents, which, if we apply with any consistency the only available definition, we have no proper reason for refusing to include among the viruses.

The first group consists of the so-called bacteriophages, transmissible agents by which cultures of visible bacteria can become infected, which cause disintegration or lysis of the bacteria which they infect, and, in so doing, undergo a very rapid multiplication. The phenomenon was discovered by Twort, working in London, but its earliest detailed investigation was made by D'Herelle, whose name, bacteriophages, has been generally adopted. By an important school of investigators, headed by Bordet, the bacteriophages are regarded as providing a typical example of the production of a transmissible infective agent by a kind of heterogenesis. D'Herelle regarded a bacteriophage as a separate infective agent, requiring for its propagation access to bacteria susceptible to its infective action, but, under those conditions, propagating itself. Bordet and his followers, on the other hand, regard a bacteriophage as a toxic, lytic principle, produced by a perverted vital process of a bacillus and causing its disintegration, and capable then of infecting other bacilli of the same kind and constraining them in turn to a similar metabolic perversion, by which the agent of their own destruction is then reproduced. The rival theories as to the nature of the bacteriophages are, accordingly, closely similar to those which divide opinion concerning the nature of the other viruses.

The second group consists of the filterable agents obtained from certain malignant tumours, particularly of birds, by the infective action of which, when injected into the tissues of a healthy bird, the appearance of a similar tumour is caused, from which in turn, when it has grown to sufficient size, the filterable infective agent can again be extracted. Here again we have the same dual possibility of interpretation for the facts. There are those who regard the tumour-producing agent as an extrinsic virus infecting the cells and exciting the morbid propensity to unrestrained growth which gives them their malignant, tumour-forming properties. There are others who regard the tumour-formation as due primarily to a perversion of the metabolism of certain cells, and believe that products of this perverted activity, infecting another cell, can constrain its metabolism to a similar perversion. Mechanical or chemical irritation can induce the beginning of a tumour, on the one view by giving a foothold in the injured cells to a pre-existent but hitherto dormant virus; on the other view, by so altering the activities of the cells that they produce the virus as a new thing. Again we have, with regard to these agents of tumour-transmission, a duality of conception of the same kind as that which has arisen concerning the nature of more typical viruses.

We can now obtain a better view of the whole problem, by considering the sizes of the infective units of the different viruses for which measurements are available, including in the list the agents transmitting certain avian tumours, and the bacteriophages, as well as those causal agents of infectious diseases which would more generally be regarded as typical viruses. In the construction of Table I my colleague Dr. Elford has kindly given me his assistance. At the head of the table, for comparison, I have put typical, smallish representatives of the ordinary bacteria, with diameters of about 1·5 and 0·75 micron, or, to adopt at once a notation which will be more suitable for the smaller virus units, 1500 and 750 millimicrons. At about $\frac{2}{3}$ that diameter, 500 millimicrons, we should come to the smallest of the ordinary bacteria. It is then but a small step down to the largest unit size of an accepted virus, that of psittacosis, at about 275 millimicrons. Of about the same dimensions are the so-called Rickettsia organisms, of typhus and trench-fever, which, for some reason not too clear, are not usually included among the viruses, though they have all the characteristics of these.

We come then to a rather numerous group of viruses, with units of diameter between 150 and 100 millimicrons. A number of these have been made visible to ordinary microscopy by special staining methods, and have been successfully photographed in the living condition by using a shorter wave-length of the ultraviolet region. Note that in this dimensional group are included the agents which transmit some of the fowl tumours, and the virus of herpes, both of these being regarded, by eminent authority, as typical examples of autogenous cell-products. You will notice that fairly high in the series, just below the virus of fowl plague, comes the most coarsely particulate of the bacteriophages yet examined, and that the most finely particulate of these agents is on the same dimensional level as the viruses of poliomyelitis (infantile paralysis) and foot-and-mouth disease.

You will see that, even at this early stage in the discovery and

study of viruses, the series is almost a continuous one, from viruses, at the upper end, which cannot logically be refused the status of very small organisms, to those at the lower end of the scale, far below the limits of detection by microscopical methods yet available. The dimensions of the infective units of these more finely particulate viruses are but small multiples of those of the molecules of ordinary proteins; they appear to be smaller, indeed, than the very large molecules of haemocyanin, the respiratory blood pigment of certain invertebrates. The data given for the various proteins in solution are those obtained by Svedberg with the ultracentrifuge. Since ultrafiltration through membranes has given closely similar dimensions for the same proteins, the accuracy of the latter method is independently confirmed.

Looking at the matter from the point of view of an interested observer, not being myself engaged in the investigation of the viruses, but having daily opportunities of contact and discussion with those who are, I form the definite impression that the chief difficulty, in the way of accepting them as self-propagating organisms, is that due to the minute dimensions of some. The members of the group have so many properties in common that, whichever view of their nature we adopt, we shall find it difficult not to apply it to the whole series. Thus, if we begin our consideration of the series from the upper end, we shall find it difficult not to regard them as self-propagating organisms, dependent on the infected cells only for the conditions which make that propagation possible; and we shall then find difficulty in postulating such organisation and power of self-reproduction when we reach the lower end of the series, and find viruses in a state of physical dispersion approaching that of a protein in solution. If we begin our consideration at the lower end, the difficulty of postulating organisation and self-propagation, at such minute dimensions, meets us at the outset. We may then be inclined to picture the viruses as not reproducing themselves, but as perverting the metabolism of the cells they infect, so that these reproduce the agents of their own perversion; and then, at the upper end of the series, we meet viruses behaving like these in every respect, except that the microscope can apparently show them to us with the forms of definite and independent organisms. It may be suggested that we are, in fact, dealing with fundamentally different things at the two ends of the series—with ultramicroscopic and strictly parasitic bacteria at the upper end, and with autogenous toxic principles in solution at the lower end. This seems to me, frankly, to be a weak evasion of the difficulty, rather than a solution. It ignores the primary fact that these viruses exhibit a remarkable uniformity of properties and behaviour, apart from the dimensions of their units, and it leaves us with no means of determining, or even guessing, at what level of unitary dimensions the fundamental change occurs, from self-propagating infective organisms, to autogenous transmissible toxins. Let us take but one example. From its position in the list, with a unit dimension of 85 millimicrons, we should find difficulty in excluding the virus of Ulcerative Stomatitis from a group showing organisation. Only just above it in the series we come to viruses of which the infective units have been certainly seen and photographed. The virus of foot-and-mouth disease, on the other hand, at the bottom of our series, would be a typical case of an unorganized principle, if we made the suggested division. Yet so similar are these two viruses in other respects, including the nature of the diseases which they cause in horses and cattle respectively, that they have only recently been distinguished as separate infective agents.

If time allowed, I could quote evidence of resistance to various kinds of physical treatment, which has been held to support the view, concerning one virus-like agent or another, that it is an unorganized product of the infected cell, and not a self-propagating organism; and in every such case I think I could put forward parallel evidence of a similar resistance, in the case of viruses for which most observers would now admit that an organized independence is practically certain. I could put before you also evidence concerning the immunological reactions, of some even of the most finely particulate viruses, remaining constant or unaffected by infective transmission through different host species. I could quote, again, the fact that an individual animal or plant, having a natural or acquired immunity to a virus, may harbour that virus in its apparently healthy tissues, ready to show its full virulence on inoculation into a subject susceptible to its attack; or, yet again, the fact that a virus such as that of rabies can apparently be permanently exterminated in a country like our own, never to reappear, unless by the criminal folly of an evasion of quarantine. And such facts seem, in the light of present knowledge, not easy to reconcile with the view that these viruses are products of the cellular activities of the hosts which they infect.

I believe, as a matter of opinion, that a judicial review of such subsidiary lines of evidence would show a balance in favour of the homogenetic conception of viruses as organized and self-propagating, and against the heterogenetic conception of them as products of the infected cells of the host. Having no time for such a full review, let us suppose that these different additional items neutralize or cancel one another, and leave us with the main problem, due to the minute dimensions of the infective particles of certain viruses. There is one aspect of these dimensional data which has, perhaps, received insufficient attention. All viruses are obligate parasites, and whatever the nature of their propagation, it takes place in the cells which they infect. The free particles which are measured by differential filtration have no vegetative or reproductive activity. The statement that they are infective means that they can develop those vital activities in the protoplasm of a susceptible cell; but there we cannot yet measure them by the filter or the microscope. Our theoretical problem is, therefore, not to determine the lower limit of size compatible with whatever physical and enzymatic system we may picture as the minimum required for a living, reproductive cellular unit; the problem is rather to determine what is the minimal portion of such a unit which might be adequate for its reconstitution under favourable conditions, though itself incapable of a separate vital activity. The statement has frequently been made, on good authority, that relatively complex, visible organisms, such as spirochaets or bacilli, can break up into ultramicroscopic particles, from which the vegetative and reproductive organism can grow again under favourable conditions; and the lack of general acceptance of such claims has been due to conflict of evidence rather than theoretical difficulty. I am aware that speculation along such lines very quickly carries us beyond the reach of present knowledge, and that no positive theory of such a kind could be justified. I am inclined, however, to doubt whether any greater justification can be found for an attitude which would exclude such a possibility as unthinkable, and would be prepared to regard the smallness of the units which can transmit infection by some viruses as finally excluding all possibility of these viruses being self-propagating organisms, even under the conditions of their active growth and multiplication in the infected cells, where as yet we can neither see nor measure them.

It cannot be claimed that either of these rival conceptions of the nature of the viruses is free from difficulties. Our choice between them must have the character of a prophecy rather than a conviction dealing with probabilities rather than with established facts; and in making such a prophetic choice, I think that we may properly follow Huxley in giving due weight to historical analogy. Biogenesis, as Huxley has told us, has been repeatedly on its trial, under increasingly difficult conditions of defence, as attention has been directed to smaller and smaller living units. Hitherto it has won at each successive stage. Now it is faced with a new challenge, in which the smallness of the units concerned can be used, in itself, as an argument against their self-propagation. Yet even here, as we have seen, improving methods have already revealed as organisms some viruses to which organisation would have been denied but a few years ago; and I incline to the belief that biogenesis will yet again establish its validity, even in cases where, in the light of present knowledge, the method of its maintenance is still difficult to comprehend. New facts are needed, and new methods to obtain them; and it is a hopeful feature of the situation that both are being won. The clash of theory is giving an added zest to the search, and a wide and progressive advance is on foot. It is more knowledge that we need, to give mankind a new control over this subtle and varied menace to life and health, and to allow us to see the real meaning of what is still a deep biological mystery. I cannot better conclude than with another quotation from Huxley's address, on which I have already drawn so largely: ... "And thus mankind will have one more admonition that 'the people perish for lack of knowledge'; and that the alleviation of the miseries, and the promotion of the welfare, of men must be sought by those who will not lose their pains, in that diligent, patient, loving study of all the multitudinous aspects of Nature, the results of which constitute exact knowledge, or Science."

EXTRACTS FROM FIVE WAR-TIME

PRESIDENTIAL ADDRESSES
TO THE ROYAL SOCIETY

(1941–1945)

1941

THOUGH the first and imperative call on the science of all free countries is for the means of winning the war, to save the freedom without which science cannot in any true sense survive, we cannot put aside the duty of preparing for the part which science must play, in rebuilding and maintaining civilization when peace returns. The conference recently organized by the British Association, on "Science and World Order," attracted more attention from the Press and the public than is usually given to scientific events and discussions; and it was, indeed, an impressive and significant fact that men of science from a dozen or more different countries, some far distant, should have found it possible now to meet, here in our war-scarred London, and to find the time and the impulse for such debate. We may offer our very sincere congratulations on the success of such an enterprise. Many who took part in these meetings, held at a time when science finds itself conscript and organized as never before for the destructive purposes of war, were clearly ready to support the view that it should be as fully organized by the governments of a world at peace, for its proper purposes of enriching life and enlarging the opportunities of happiness for all men alike. There were not wanting voices, however, such as that of our Biological Secretary*, to sound a warning of dangers which might be entailed, by such fullness of association between science and government as others were advocating with conviction and enthusiasm. Freedom and opportunity, it was pointed out, rather than organization, provide the conditions for the highest types of research, and thus, in the end, for the greatest services

---

* Then Prof. A. V. Hill, C.H., F.R.S.

which science can give to mankind. I find myself in sympathy
with this view, and nobody here, I think, would suggest that it is
usually possible to organize the researches which advance boldly
into the unknown, and open new vistas to human understanding.
Here we shall certainly not overlook the fact that, in the period
between the two wars, important funds have been placed at the
disposal of the Royal Society by a series of generous benefactors,
to be administered for the support of researches over a wide
range of subjects, in complete independence of any control
by the state.

On the other hand, I think that it will be agreed that the
remarkable development in this country, since 1914, of the state
support of research administered by the three Research Councils,
normally in relation to the needs and the activities of a nation at
peace, has taken place without any obvious detriment or danger
to the freedom of science. The Royal Society's former function,
of advising the Government directly on all scientific matters, and
of organizing such systematic researches as were then undertaken in the public interest, has, of necessity, been shared and
greatly diminished. We, as a Society, however, can fairly regard
this development as, in many respects, a realization of the plans
and the dreams of our predecessors here; and I do not think it
fanciful to claim that our Society's traditions and standards have
been still effective, through the influence of our Fellows on the
Research Councils and their Committees, and through the filling
of their chief executive offices by men of our Fellowship. As a
whole-time research worker myself, since 1914, under the body
which became the Medical Research Council, and the senior
now in that service, I can bear grateful witness to the freedom of
opportunity which can exist under an enlightened organization
and control, exercised on behalf of the Government. I have no
reason to suppose that the conditions are otherwise under the
other Research Councils. Nor should we lose sight of the fact
that a further large proportion of the free scientific research of
the country is now indebted to support from the state through
grants to the universities, administered without any trace of
detailed Government control.

While, therefore, the existing mechanisms for the support of
science by the state are doubtless susceptible of improvement at
one point or another, I find no reason to fear any threat to the

freedom of science from them, or from any natural development on those lines. Nor do I fear it from a wider use of the organized application of science and scientific method to problems of public welfare; nor, again, from a more effective access of scientific knowledge to those responsible for government. A year ago Sir William Bragg told the Society of the formation of the Scientific Advisory Committee to the War Cabinet, under the chairmanship of Lord Hankey, with the President and two Secretaries of this Society as members *ex officio*. The representation of the Society has, indeed, been strengthened since then, and in a manner most welcome, by the fact that, though I have succeeded him *ex officio*, Sir William Bragg still gives his wisdom and experience to the work of that Committee, as an extra member.

There is one direction, however, in which I do find some reason to fear for the freedom of science. If science should become entangled in controversial politics, through the over-eagerness of its advocates and champions to invoke the sanction of science, or to claim its potentialities, in support of any special political doctrine, then indeed I believe that the threat to its freedom might become a real danger. Let there be no misunderstanding of my meaning. I am not abusing the privilege of this Chair by using "controversial" as an epithet, to be applied to political opinions which I do not happen to share. I see danger if the name of science, or the very cause of its freedom, should become involved as a battle-cry in a campaign on behalf of any political system, whether its opponents would describe it as revolutionary or reactionary. If science were allowed thus to be used as a weapon of political pressure, it would be impossible to protect science itself eventually from the pressure of sectional politics. If that should happen the dangers are, I believe, beyond dispute—the danger, for example, that fundamental researches, having no immediately practical appeal, would be allowed to fall into arrears through relative neglect; or the danger that the rigid standards of true science would be relaxed, by allowing the convenience of results for policy or for propaganda to enter into the assessment of their validity as evidence. This Society, with its firm and unbroken tradition of complete aloofness from political controversy, may still find it an important part of its function, to keep watch and, if necessary, to stand without compromise, for the right and the duty of science to seek the truth for its own sake, in complete freedom from any kind of extraneous influence. I hope, indeed, that there will never be need thus to invoke our tradition, in order to protect the freedom and the integrity of science from the enthusiasm and the advocacy of any of its friends.

1942

(Introduction to the Tercentenary Lectures on Isaac Newton.)

WE are to-day within a few weeks of the three hundredth anniversary of the birth of Isaac Newton. Wherever the progress of our Western science and philosophy has become effective, men will remember what that event was to mean for the world. Newton, as we shall hear, at the age of 43, when he had determined to abandon all further concern with natural philosophy, was induced at length, by Halley's friendly insistence, to give written form and system to the mathematical discoveries with which his amazing mind had been occupied over a period of some twenty years. The result was one of the greatest intellectual achievements in the history of mankind—the *Principia*, providing for more than two centuries a framework for the mechanical interpretation of the universe and a basis for the building of physical science, and therewith of the material structure of our modern civilization.

We in Britain regard Isaac Newton as still, beyond challenge, the greatest of our men of science. Nor should the claim be limited to this island or to the British Commonwealth of Nations; for it was not till nearly half a century after Newton's death that former British colonists in North America began their development of an independent nation; and Newton is theirs as well as ours.

But, while we may proudly claim him as the countryman of all who share the birthright of the English tongue, the discoveries of science have belonged, and must belong again, to the whole world, and Newton's achievement is a part of the common heritage of all peoples. It cannot be doubted that, if it had fallen in normal times, this tercentenary would have been marked by the greatest of international gatherings, in which men of science and philosophers from all the world would have assembled to do honour to Newton's memory. It would have been natural then to expect leadership, in such an enterprise, from the only two institutions which were intimately concerned with Newton's career as a man of science—Trinity College, in Cambridge, and this our Royal Society of London. Our two foundations did, indeed, confer as to the wisdom of attempting by joint action, even in this year of war, to arrange such a restricted and domestic celebration as the present conditions would allow. We agreed, however, to put aside such planning for the present, carrying it forward in our hopes to the time when a world at peace may be able to join in international commemoration of an event which has meant so much for all mankind. May the time be not too far distant.

To-day we are holding the 280th Anniversary Meeting of the Royal Society, on Saint Andrew's Day as by regular custom, ever since the first meeting on that day in 1662. It seemed to us that we should depart, on this occasion, a little from the usual order of our proceedings, so that, on a day so near to the tercentenary of his birth, our Fellows and our guests may be reminded of Newton. We have accordingly asked three of our Fellows to address the Society on different aspects of Newton's work, in its relations to the science of the past and the present. We have asked Professor Andrade to give us the opportunity of understanding the magnitude of the change which Newton's work produced, in the conceptions of the material universe which were current in his own times. We know that to his contemporaries Newton's discoveries came as a great revelation, and we hope that Professor Andrade will help us to understand why they did so. We have asked Lord Rayleigh to deal, by demonstration where possible, with the experimental work of Newton and the great discoveries which he made by that method. This is an aspect of his greatness which popular estimates have tended to overlook; but I think that Lord Rayleigh will be able to convince us that Newton as an experimenter would have had claims to a place among our greatest men of science, even if he had failed, as he so nearly did fail, to write the *Principia*. And, finally, we have asked Sir James Jeans to give us some reassessment of the validity and permanence of Newton's system, in relation to the immense advances of knowledge in our own times. There are many who have not the mathematical equipment to follow them in detail, who are nevertheless aware that revolutionary changes have been taking place in conceptions of the mechanics of the universe and of its ultimate material units. How is the Newtonian system affected by the discoveries which have required the general theory of relativity and the quantum mechanics at opposite ends of the stupendous scale? Is it being supplemented, modified, or superseded after its centuries of dominance? We hope that Sir James Jeans will tell us; and we may remember, perhaps with comfort, that Newton's *Principia* seemed difficult and abstruse to his contemporaries, and that he even confessed that he had made it so deliberately, "to avoid being bated by little smatterers in mathematics."

Before I call on our chosen lecturers to address us, there are two other matters relating to Newton and the Royal Society, which it seems proper to mention here. In the hamlet of Woolsthorpe, near Colsterworth on the Great North Road, some six miles south of Grantham, there is still a modest manor farmhouse, with a small orchard in front of it. Here the Newtons lived, simple yeomen farmers, and here, two months after his father had died, Isaac Newton was born, a puny, premature infant, on Christmas Day, 1642, twenty years before the Royal Society was incorporated by the grant of its first Charter. The house stands but little altered since that day. The room in which Newton was born has a simple marble tablet on the wall, inscribed with Pope's well-known couplet. But this house had importance in Newton's later life and in his work, and not only as his birthplace. It was here that he returned from his schooling at Grantham, at the age of 16, to take charge of the farm for his mother; and here, to the incalculable gain of science and the world, he showed such incompetence as a farmer that he was sent back to school, and thence to Cambridge. It was here, again, that he returned in the autumn of 1665, when the plague drove him from Cambridge; and here, during the following eighteen months of quiet exile in the country, his early ripening genius grasped already the essential principles of his major theoretical discoveries. You can still see the upper chamber which he then used as a study; and in the little orchard there is an old, recumbent apple tree, which, they will tell you, is descended by direct grafting from that which Newton saw. The land which Newton's family farmed is rapidly being laid waste, alas, by quarrying for ironstone; and soon there will be little left unspoiled save the orchard and garden round the house. It has seemed to us that, in this year of commemoration, something should be done to preserve for posterity a house and garden which carry such momentous memories, and which have meant so much for science. We have accordingly formed a small Committee, in which Sir John Russell and Sir James Jeans have joined with the Officers of the Royal Society. We have been in friendly negotiation with the lord of the manor, Major Turnor —a name associated in several past generations with the Royal Society and with Isaac Newton—as to the possibility of acquiring this now tiny but historic property, so that it may be put for as long as possible beyond the risk of damage or decay. Major Turnor has generously offered to sell the property for this purpose at a price substantially less than its value, and only this morning I received a letter from Lord Macmillan which enables me to announce that the Pilgrim Trust will be responsible for the sum required for the purchase.

Then I think that it is our special duty here, at this Anniversary Meeting, to remember that, while Newton's great discoveries belong to the world, they came to publication through the Royal Society, and that Newton occupied its presidential Chair for the last twenty-four years of his long life. Though his *Opticks* was not published till after he had become President, his original work for science was practically finished by the time of his election, and he had for some years been Master of the Mint. There can be no doubt, however, that the wide fame of his achievements, and the respect and admiration in which he was everywhere held, did much, at a critical period in its history, to establish the prestige of this Society in the eyes of the world. Let us then remember to-day that Isaac Newton, the greatest man of science of our race, was also the greatest of the Royal Society's presidents.

1943

LAST year we devoted this Anniversary Meeting to a simple celebration such as the war conditions allowed of the three hundredth anniversary of the birth of Isaac Newton. We have noted with appreciative interest that other countries also marked the tercentenary year by paying homage to our Newton's memory. Particular mention is due to the commemorative meetings held, under the tremendous stress of war, not only by the Moscow Academy of Sciences, but also in a number of other scientific centres of Soviet Russia, one as far away as Novo-Sibirsk. The Council's report mentions the gift which we have sent to the Soviet Academy of Sciences of Moscow, in recognition of this union with our colleagues of Soviet Russia in commemorating one of the greatest scientific achievements of all time, as in the present devotion of all that science can give, in both our countries, to the winning of this war for freedom.

Not since 1941 have I addressed the Society from this Chair, at its Anniversary Meeting, according to regular custom*. Only a week after we met here in 1941, the United States of America had become our ally; less than a year later came a turning-point of the war, with Stalingrad and El Alamein; and now the end seems no longer to be in doubt, though we cannot tell how long it may be in coming. I think that it is proper now to claim for science its due share in the achievements which have created the present prospect, in such vivid contrast with that of two years ago. Science in the countries of our great alliance has been devoted without reserve during these two years to the winning of the war; in this country it had been so already for the two years which preceded them. No longer are the allies straining now to overtake a lead gained by the enemy in years of stealthy prepara-tion; the lead is rather on our side. If such things could be weighed and measured, I believe that we should find the alliance to be as far ahead of our enemy in the present volume of our united war researches, and in the brain power of the highest class now concentrated upon them, as in the more readily ponder-able output of war material by our industries. And no more than our armed forces or our factories can science afford to relax or to divide its effort until the total victory has been won, without which we can have no faith in the world's future. The increasing certainty of the end, however, imposes upon us with a growing urgency the duty of looking also to that future, and to the part which science must play in the nation and the world when peace returns.

---

* The Anniversary Meeting in 1942 had been transferred to the Lecture Theatre of the Royal Institution, to accommodate a larger audience and provide facilities for lecture experiments, in connexion with the war-time commemoration of the Newton Tercentenary.

From different influential quarters, as from the Parliamentary and Scientific Committee and from the Federation of British Industries, we have had important pronouncements on the urgent need for national enterprise and national spending on higher education in science and technology, and on the encouragement of research in the applications of science to industry. No body of scientific men will need arguments to convince them that we must think in such matters on a scale, not merely larger, but of a higher order than any with which we have hitherto been familiar. We of the Royal Society shall certainly give enthusiastic endorsement to any movement in that direction. From its beginning to the present day our Society has always taken a lively interest in the applications of science to the general enrichment of human life, and the enlargement of the means of human happiness. One of the expressed objects of the extension, in recent years, of the number annually elected into our Fellowship, was the maintenance of that interest, under the growing pressure for recognition of achievements in the more fundamental and academic ranges of science. We shall certainly welcome, then, and join in advocating a great expansion of the nation's support of applied science, whether through the Government's Research Councils concerned with researches bearing on industry, medicine, and agriculture, or through departments concerned with the uses of science for defensive preparations in peace time and for other national interests, or with the training of recruits for research by grants of public money to the Universities. I think that it can properly be claimed that we knew here, even before the belief attracted a wider support and conviction, that a modern nation, as certainly as a well-organized modern industry, depends for success upon generous and far-seeing expenditure on scientific research and on the recruitment of first-rate ability to its service, and risks failure and disaster by parsimony and a narrow vision of its responsibilities in these directions.

The response of our national scientific reserves to the demands of war might suggest that our national deficiency hitherto has been chiefly in provision for the applications of science, and that fundamental researches in this country have lacked less in opportunity and encouragement. Here too, however, if we make comparison with other countries, I think that we shall be obliged to conclude that our discoverers, as great as any in a world era of great discovery, have often had to do their work in spite of a paucity of equipment and accommodation which would hardly have been conceivable elsewhere. That is a difficulty and a disparity which, unless some action is taken, will certainly increase with the growing demands of fundamental researches for elaborate and costly items of equipment. Recent discoveries have made such items available, and necessary, at a rate which the war-time concentration of research will even have accelerated. Money to procure and to install them will become ever more essential to work on the general front of scientific progress. The Society's Council, having considered a Memorandum by certain of its Fellows on the prospective needs of fundamental researches in physics, have already appointed a Committee to consider the position in detail. It seems unlikely that other departments of fundamental science, when news of this decision reaches their representatives, will wish the Society to assume that the needs of physics, even if more obvious than some others, are unique in their importance and urgency. With so many interests and authorities now directly concerned for applied science, we can hardly doubt, indeed, that it is to-day a primary duty and mission of the Royal Society, as of the related Societies having more special and restricted aims in science, to aid and to encourage researches which seek the advancement of knowledge without immediate reference to its use, though with a clear conviction that such progress is often a necessary condition of practical advance, or even the most direct way towards it. Care for the practical fruits of the tree of knowledge was never, indeed, so urgent as to-day; but the tree will wither unless we take care also that the roots have nourishment and room for spreading.

The mention of this last necessity brings me to the problem of the need of the Royal Society, and the more pressing need of one, at least, of our neighbour societies here, for accommodation more worthy of their national importance. The matter has more than once been under discussion in the past, and has recently been a matter of renewed concern to the Society's officers. With the efficient help of our Assistant Secretary, Mr. Griffith Davies, we have been making, in this connexion, a survey of the records dealing with the different homes of the Royal Society, from its foundation down to recent years. I think that on another occasion, when more time is available, the Society may like to hear a review in greater detail of this aspect of our history, which has many points of interest. To-day the mention of a few of these must suffice.

Early in our career the interest of the Crown in the Society, and perhaps a recognition of a duty to provide accommodation for it, were signified by King Charles the Second's grant of Chelsea College and its estates, as set forth in our third Charter of 1669. The property proved, alas, for various reasons, to be much more a burden than an asset, and Christopher Wren, in 1682, with the Council's approval and recorded gratitude, sold it back to the King for £1,300. Meanwhile an opportunity for the Society to acquire a house of its own, built to the designs of Hooke and Wren, on a piece of land granted by Henry Howard from the grounds of Arundel House, had not become effective. The Society, therefore, save for interruptions due to the plague and the fire of London, remained for fifty years from its foundation a tenant of rooms in Gresham College, till in 1710, when Isaac Newton was President, it acquired the house in Crane Court, off Fleet Street, which was its home for another sixty-eight years. In 1778, thanks to the personal interest in our affairs of King George III, the friend of our great President of those days, Sir Joseph Banks, the Society was granted quarters in Somerset House. Therewith the obligation of the state to provide us with housing was for the first time definitely accepted, "in generous recognition by the Sovereign of the services which science had rendered to the state," as Banks stated in his address of 1780. The records show that the accommodation in Somerset House was regarded from the first as inadequate, even though our requirements had been reduced by the transfer of our "Repository of Rarities" to the British Museum. The rooms, on the other hand, can be seen from prints of the period to have had a pleasant dignity, and the Society remained in them for nearly eighty years.

Towards the middle of the nineteenth century, a movement arose to secure new and better accommodation for the Royal Society, and at the same time for the other principal scientific societies then existing—the Linnaean, Geological, Astronomical, and Chemical Societies. As early as 1847 a memorandum was under consideration by the newly founded Philosophical Club, a more seriously minded secession from, or rival to, the Royal

Society Club of those days, formed under the same influences as those which had just carried the revised method of electing our Fellows. The Club presented proposals for bringing the major scientific societies under one roof, centralizing and coördinating their libraries without any attempt at fusion, providing three or four meeting rooms of different sizes, for use by the Societies in common and in turn, and, in general, making better provision for the interests common to all without any impairment of their independence in rules, traditions, procedures, or property. When those of us who have been considering present-day needs look at this memorandum, as finally presented in 1852, we cannot but admire the foresight and wisdom of our mid-Victorian predecessors.

An opportunity of housing the scientific societies thus, as a community of coöperative but substantially independent units, was actually presented in the same year, 1852, by the offer of accommodation in new buildings then being planned on the estate at Kensington Gore, acquired with the proceeds of the 1851 Exhibition. We begin to see the benevolent interest of the Prince Consort in our concerns. Kensington Gore, we must remember, in those days of horse transport, was still on the rural margin of the suburbs; and, in gratefully declining the offer, the Royal Society and its associates urged upon the Government the desirability of housing the scientific societies centrally and, if possible, under a single roof. The acquisition by the Government, some years earlier, of Burlington House and its grounds, extending from the Piccadilly frontage through to the street which is now named Burlington Gardens, seemed, indeed, to have provided the ideal opportunity for giving effect to such a plan. The Prince Consort, with a vision of the future meaning of science far in advance of his time, privately urged the five scientific societies to press their claim to the site. It had been understood, indeed, that the primary intention of the Government in buying Burlington House had been to provide accommodation for the learned societies. Lord Wrottesley, then our President, personally canvassed the Government, making it clear "that the desire of the chartered societies for juxtaposition and for the Burlington House site was unabated." Failing that, he indicated, they would be glad to be lodged in the buildings then occupied by the Royal Academy, that is, in what is now the

National Gallery. The existence of a rival claim had become clear, and had, indeed, been mentioned to the Royal Society by the Prince Consort. It appears that the Government had already made some kind of commitment to the Royal Academy, so far as the mansion of Burlington House was concerned. It would take much too long to discuss even what is known of the rival lobbyings of those days. It must suffice for this occasion to recall the results, and to lament the fact that a magnificent opportunity was lost, which would have given London a scientific centre worthy of the nation's achievement. We cannot blame our predecessors, who probably did all that was possible; nor can we grudge their success to our friends of the Royal Academy, who are in no way to blame for taking what was offered to them. If the Government, indeed, had then used Burlington House and its grounds to discharge only these two of the obligations to which they were to some degree committed, the needs both of the scientific societies and of the Royal Academy could still have been handsomely met, and adequate scope for future development could have been ensured to both. The mansion itself with the wings of this front courtyard, already scheduled for rebuilding, could, for example, have been allotted to one, while the other of the two claimants could have had a new building, with frontage at the north end of the gardens, and ample space for extension southwards over them, to meet increasing needs and new developments. The Government, however, used Burlington House first to satisfy a third obligation which it had accepted, to house the University of London, then only a degree-giving body requiring space chiefly for the periodical examination of large numbers of candidates. Then in 1858, the continued pressure of the scientific societies and the Government's own desire to recover the rooms in Somerset House, led them to offer the use of Burlington House to the Royal Society, subject to the condition that for the time, and pending rebuilding on the sites round this courtyard, the Linnaean and Chemical Societies should be accommodated with us in the mansion, and that the University of London should still be able to use the large rooms in it for examinations. It is curious to reflect that this temporary arrangement gave to the Royal Society and its associates the only opportunity which they ever enjoyed, even to share the use of a room suitable for a meeting of more than very modest dimensions.

In old Burlington House, then, we were established, and were to remain there with the Chemical and Linnaean Societies for some fifteen years; and an appearance of stability had at first been given to our occupancy by the mention of plans to build a new examination hall for the University of London on the western side of this quadrangle, and to allow the Royal Society to use this also for large meetings and for its gallery of portraits. Two later developments, however, dispelled any such hopes, In 1867 evidence came to the Society, first through a statement in *The Times*, that the Government had decided, after all, to give the Royal Academy a permanent lease of Burlington House and the right to extend northwards by building over its gardens. At about the same time, and presumably in fulfilment of another commitment, the large building which now fronts on to Burlington Gardens was begun, to accommodate the University of London and its examinations, and was opened by Queen Victoria in 1870.

The scientific societies were not, indeed, to be homeless; but the only possibility now left was to accommodate them in the buildings planned to be erected round this front courtyard, where they have been ever since. The total space thus offered did, indeed, allow more room to each of the societies than it had previously enjoyed, even after the Society of Antiquaries, at the Royal Society's instance, had been included in the scheme. But the space now available could not easily be planned for the sharing of meeting rooms and general facilities, or for a central federation of the libraries, or for any of the features of the earlier plan which would have enabled the societies to function as independent members of a real scientific community. The scheme had an even more fatal defect. The plans were made on the assumption that the societies existing in the 1860's, with their respective dimensions and requirements at that date, would provide a pattern of the needs of science for all time, or at least for the life of buildings designed to mid-Victorian standards of permanence. Each of these societies, therefore, with the approval of our own we must admit, presented its separate claim and had it embodied in the solidity of the buildings we still inhabit, filling the available space completely and precluding any later expansion, rearrangement, or new admission to the circle thus finally closed. Societies which have changed but little in numbers or activities may have had little reason, even yet, to complain of the accommodation which they then acquired. For others the allotment, which had been regarded then as satisfying future needs for half a century at least, became obviously inadequate very much earlier.

In 1900 came news that the large building on the Burlington Gardens frontage was to be vacated by London University, and tentative enquiry was immediately made as to the possibility of allotting it to the Royal Society, on the ground that "the present rooms occupied by the Society were rapidly becoming inadequate." The Government, however, had already decided to transfer the building to their Civil Service Commissioners, and it has continued to be dedicated to its original use for large-scale examinations, save for the later assignment of certain rooms in it to our much younger sister, the British Academy. It will be noted that the Royal Society was finding its quarters here inadequate as early as 1900, twenty-seven years after it entered them, and before there was even any prospect of the great expansion of its responsibilities and activities in recent years. Our accommodation is still the same to-day, after seventy years. Our walls cannot find room to hang our important collection of scientific portraits, and our great library is badly overcrowded, even though we have parted with some of it to give better housing, for a time, to the remainder; and it continues, of course, to grow. Library pressure, in fact, is felt to varying degrees by all the societies here; and I think that it is still true, as some of our predecessors saw already in the 1850's, that no scheme will be able to deal with this problem efficiently, and to meet modern needs without disturbing historic associations, which does not include some kind of central coördination of libraries. The lack of a lecture or conference room, available in common for larger meetings, and well equipped with modern resources for projection and demonstration, is another acutely felt need. There are greater needs and anomalies, however, than any of these common ones. Of all the societies here the Chemical Society, which was originally satisfied with the poorest allotment of rooms, has undergone the greatest expansion. In the 1860's it had a membership of some 450; it now has about 5000. Its library, of great importance to all workers in chemistry, whether fundamental or applied, has so burst the bounds of its accommodation, that a part of it is deposited in the crypt of a neighbouring church; and the Chemical Society's meeting room is in every way unsuitable and inadequate to the meanest conception of the regular needs of a society of its standing and numbers. Apparently our predecessors of the 1870's did not see much future for chemistry. On the same evidence, they did not foresee any future for physics at all. The Physical Society did not then exist; by the time it was born there was no room for its admission, and the State has never offered it a home. The same is true of other societies formed later to deal with functional aspects of biology and other new fields of knowledge. For most of their meetings these newer societies use and need the facilities available in academic and research institutions. A national centre of science, however, should be capable of progressive adjustment to changing needs, and we ought to be able to make new admissions, on a varying scale of allotment, to the central community of societies.

What then should we be doing to deal with the situation? Actions and decisions long past have imposed it upon us, and regrets and repinings over an opportunity lost more than seventy years ago will not help us to-day. We must admit, too, that our present quarters, with all their defects of elasticity, have provided a combination of central position with freedom from noise of traffic which might be hard to find again. Let me say, then, that the Royal Society's officers, having consulted with the officers of other societies here, and particularly of those whose needs are urgent or whose interests might be directly concerned, have not yet abandoned the attempt to find a solution which would not involve the removal of any from the Burlington House estate. If we fail in that direction—and there is no ground for optimism— the problem will remain, and the time is not one for neglect or postponement of action. On all hands we hear talk of reconstruction and see plans for the rebuilding of London. We cannot expect another Christopher Wren—one of our original Fellows and a leader in the science of his day, before he became its greatest architect; London missed that opportunity. It is natural and proper for the plans now being presented to make spacious and impressive provision in the new London for opera, drama, music, and all the fine arts; and we shall surely join in a general welcome to any practicable scheme which can open the doors more widely to such cultural privileges, and enhance their dignity and worth in the eyes of London and of the nation. But I do not think that we must stand by and allow the claims of science again to go by default. A fear of overstatement, a passion for critical accuracy which is a part of the very spirit of science, may make us reluctant advocates. If necessary, however, we must be ready to remind all who may be concerned of the part which the British scientific effort has played, in making it possible now to plan at all, with confidence, for our own civic and national reconstruction. But for science, we may remind them, the very different plans which our enemies were so recently making for our future might already be taking effect. I have no doubt that the claim will be handsomely admitted; but we ought not to be too easily appeased with compliments and oratorical bouquets. The nation's opportunity, when peace returns, of enjoying the arts and the amenities of life will be dependent on its standards of health and prosperity, and these, in turn, ever more directly on science and its applications, as certainly as these are still needed to secure our national survival and victory in this war.

This ancient Royal Society of London, and those societies which have grown from it and round it in later years, constitute a scientific organism which is a national and imperial heritage, second to none in the world's esteem. Here are the roots of the spreading tree of science and technology, which should form a major component of our national contribution to the new world now in the making. Seventy years ago these roots were given only enough soil for the replanting then undertaken; they have long been badly pot-bound, and some parts of the root system are threatened with strangulation, while others have appeared outside the pot. We can properly claim, I think, that the progressive needs of our scientific societies shall be given early consideration in any new allotment which plans for reconstruction may allow. We ought to have a scientific centre permitting them to coördinate their activities with economy, and giving room for change, expansion, and organic growth by budding and division, in accordance with nature's law. I think that we have the further right to expect that the home of science, in this capital city, will have a dignity symbolizing its value to the nation and the empire, and enabling us to hold up our heads in the company of other countries, whose scientific academies, not more famous than ours, have so long been housed more worthily, and with a more generous recognition of their due place in an enlightened people's scale of cultural values.

1944

THOUGH Penicillin has rightly made a special appeal to the imagination and sympathetic interest of a wide public, it is, of course, only one out of a varied range of inventions and discoveries, hastened by the stimulus of war's demands and produced, in many cases, behind the veil of its secrecy, but ready, when peace returns, to take their proper place as new gifts to the welfare and the civilized progress of mankind. From what has already been made generally known, it is clear that we may look forward to revolutionary advances in the means of communication and in the speed and safety of travel across the world, and in methods of controlling insect pests and the diseases which insects convey; and these are but a few examples of the gains which we and the world may hope to set against the tragic loss and sacrifice of the years of war. There are probably few who even suspected in 1939, that science, in countries then so dangerously unready, would find itself, before the war ended, in its present position of central importance. None of us, I think, would claim more for science even now, than to have played in this war a part of growing predominance in the provision for the fighting men of the material means of warfare, without which their heroism and sacrifice could not have prevailed. Even that duty, loyally accepted, is one from which the scientific community of the free nations must long for the release which victory will bring. But, while the operations of war have come to depend on science to a degree beyond all earlier experience, it cannot be doubted that little more than a beginning has yet been made in exploiting the possibilities of destruction, which science could progressively offer, if the world should continue thus to misuse it, and if science were still on offer for such ends. Allow me to quote a passage from a letter which the Prime Minister, whom we are proud to number among our Fellows, wrote a year ago to Professor Hill, in sending his greetings to Indian men of science.

"It is the great tragedy of our time," wrote Mr. Churchill, "that the fruits of science should by a monstrous perversion have been turned on so vast a scale to evil ends. But that is no

fault of science. Science has given to this generaation the means
of unlimited disaster or of unlimited progress. When this
war is won we shall have averted disaster. There will remain
the greater task of directing knowledge lastingly towards the
purposes of peace and human good." Noble words indeed,
and a profession of faith which will find an immediate echo
in the hope and the desire of every true man of science. "When
this war is over we shall have averted disaster"—surely that
is a confidence which every one of us will long to share. It
must be clear, however, that Mr. Churchill's reference was
to the present threat of disaster, from which the prospect of
our escape is even more fully assured to-day than when he
wrote, a year ago. We may be certain that nobody sees more
clearly than he, that the threat of final disaster to all man's hopes
and achievements will not be for ever averted, if the possibility
of the "monstrous perversion" of science is allowed to remain
and to continue its evil growth. Even in the past year our
enemies have thrown a new and vivid light on future possibilities, by the new weapons which science has enabled them
to put on trial for our destruction. Though a people's unflinching
courage and an answering effort of science and organization,
together with the progress of the allied armies over the launching
areas, have given us confidence that flying bombs and the like
will not affect the issue of this war, the warning which they
give, as to what the future might hold, is not the less clear.
The writing on the wall must be plain for all to read. If, when
the memories of the present war begin to fade, the world should
allow science again to be exploited by a nation grasping at
predominance by conquest, science will no longer be invoked
only as an aid to what valour can achieve by land, sea, or air,
but as an agent, in itself, of blind annihilation at an ever lengthening range. When we men of science regain that freedom,
for the ultimate preservation of which we have loyally accepted,
through these tragic years, the bonds of secrecy and submission
to authority, we cannot put aside with these our proper share
in the new responsibility for the future of mankind, which
this war's experiences have laid upon the men of good will
in all nations. It is true, indeed, that neither the present abuse
of science, nor any possibility of final disaster to civilization
which might come of a future perversion of its powers, can

4

be charged as a fault to science itself; no more, indeed, than we could properly charge to religion, as such, the wars which once devastated much of Europe in its name. But we men of science cannot escape from our growing share in the responsibility, in "the greater task," as Mr. Churchill has written, "of directing knowledge lastingly towards the purposes of peace and human good." No man of science has the right to prescribe for another his interpretation in detail of that duty; but there is one aim which may unite us, perhaps for the most effective action within our common grasp, and one which is worthy of all our common influence and effort. Let me quote again from Mr. Churchill's letter: "in this task," he writes, "the scientists of the world, united by the bond of a single purpose which overrides all bounds of race and language, can play a leading and inspiring part." To build anew, and on a firm and broadening foundation, a world community in science, is surely an aim worthy of our utmost effort and devotion; but there can be no swerving from the present duty, and the call on science by war may yet be sterner, before we have won the freedom thus to work for the future of the world.

1945

LAST year at this time, though the outcome of the war seemed to be no longer in doubt, there was still no clear prospect of relief for science from the effort, abnormal in direction as well as in intensity, needed to ensure and to hasten victory. Now we face the new position created by the advent of victory a few months ago, with a sudden completeness beyond all prediction. We hold our Anniversary Meeting to-day, for the first time for six years, with our mace on the table, and all the other treasures of our long history safely returned to us by their war-time custodians, to all of whom our thanks are due. We think of the part played by scientists of the Allied Nations in the winning of the war, and with a particular pride of the contribution made by scientists of the British Empire and of this Society; and we remember that Winston Churchill accepted election to our Fellowship during the year in which he stood as leader of open resistance by the British Empire alone, to the attack which threatened to submerge the freedom of the world. If it seemed proper, I could devote all the time at my disposal to-day to a review of the various activities of this ancient Society in relation to the demands on science of a modern war, from the date of our acceptance from the Government of the responsibility for preparing the scientific section of the General Register, at a time when the clouds of war were only gathering, down even to the present day.

And now the scientists of the world have before them the task of readjustment which, we may hope, will mean the whole-hearted devotion of the available resources of scientific research and development to their proper and beneficent uses. It has become a commonplace that the urgent needs of war have greatly accelerated discoveries and inventions which will now promote the advancement of science and its applications in peace. Some of these scientific swords and spears will be thus immediately applicable as peaceful implements, or with only a minimum of beating and bending—radar, for example, to the safety of transport by sea and air, and all the new wealth of chemotherapeutic agents and insecticides to peace-time hygiene and agriculture. There will certainly be many others of a less direct and obvious kind—discoveries and developments arising as side issues from the urgent uses of science in war, but capable now of applications which may open new possi-bilities of scientific advance for its own sake, or for a whole range of peaceful purposes. As mentioned in the Council Report, the Royal Society has recently agreed to collaborate with the Service Departments concerned, in setting up Com-mittees to organize such peaceful uses, of the special facilities for purely scientific observation and experiment, as are presented by Service flying, including aerial photography, by the voyages undertaken by the ships and officers of the Royal Navy in the course of their normal duties, and by the large surplus of ex-plosives—of the pre-atomic type, be it understood—which a great war leaves in hand. Let me make brief mention, by way of another example, of an unexpected gift to science, arising as a curious side-issue from the large-scale application in war of knowledge which science had provided. Some thirty years ago my former colleague, Dr. Charles Todd, published in our *Proceedings* two papers dealing with the antigenic individuality observed, even within the limits of a single breed of chickens, when the red blood corpuscles of one bird are injected into another. This was an observation, one might think, of an interest purely theoretical, though great; but the widespread application of blood transfusion during the war, to replace blood lost by the wounded, civilians now as well as warriors, has given to phenomena of this type a practical importance. Apart from the familiar natural incompatibilities, due to the known human blood groups, it was found necessary to be alert for reactions in persons who, having had an earlier transfusion, might have acquired, by an immunity reaction, a new incompatibility to the donor's red blood corpuscles. The case of such reactions hitherto most completely studied concerns an antigenic factor which Landsteiner and his colleagues had discovered, early in the war, in the red corpuscles of the *Rhesus* monkey, and had accordingly termed *Rh*. This factor they found to be present, as a Mendelian dominant, in the corpuscles of most white people, but absent from those of a minority. So, in the slang of the subject, about 85 per cent of people of the white races are "*Rh*-positive," while 15 per cent are "*Rh*-negative." Now it appears that the blood serum of an *Rh*-negative person, if he receives a transfusion of *Rh*-positive blood, acquires immune substances destructive to the "positive" red corpuscles. In consequence, he suffers a dangerous reaction if given a second, similar transfusion. And this observation has brought to light the much more important fact that, when an *Rh*-negative woman, whose husband is *Rh*-positive, becomes pregnant by him of an *Rh*-positive child, her serum is liable therewith to acquire, and to transmit through the placenta, an antibody destructive of the child's red corpuscles, so that the offspring of such a union are prone to a high rate of mortality, before or soon after birth. Whether those who survive the infantile malady, thus produced, show a greater liability to other hereditary defects, or whether deleterious maternal antibodies of this type can be formed in relation to other kinds of cells than the red blood corpuscles, are matters on which investigation must be awaited. I mention the matter to-day as an example of the gleanings which peaceful science may expect from fields of knowledge which war has been tilling and reaping. Unless I am mistaken, the widespread use of blood transfusion has thus been largely responsible for enabling human genetics now to explore a new category of congenital defects, due, not to the coincident presence of a detrimental gene in both parents, but to the possession by a father of one which is harmless, unless it excites an immunity response in a mother who lacks it.

Whether by following in new directions clues which have thus been discovered under the stimulus of war, or by resumption of researches which the war interrupted, it is clearly a matter of urgent importance that our scientific activities should now, as rapidly and as smoothly as possible, reacquire the character proper to peace. There are directions in which official action can accelerate a process of such outstanding significance to the position which our nation will be able to achieve and to hold in a world civilization, now so clearly entering its scientific era. We need our leaders and teachers in science back in the universities, and the students whom they can inspire and train, as rapidly as these can be released from war-time duty and service.

A number of our leading scientists have learned much from war-time experience of organization and team-work in research, and have been freely devoting great abilities to planning and to securing proper conditions for researches by others. It is unlikely that the debt of the nation and of its allies to the work of many of these will ever be fully known, beyond the limits of certain circles. The experience of these men should help them still to serve the nation in peace, by counsel and by advocacy, when the needs of scientific reconstruction demand these. I venture to hope, however, that there will be no such demands on the time and the energies of those who should now be our leaders in research, as to keep them away from their benches and their studies, and to deprive of their inspiration the younger men who should now be their pupils and collaborators. When the world emerged from the last war, the scientists who in this and other countries were then at the height of their powers for research, who, in Newton's fine phrase about himself, were "in the prime of their age for invention," were back in their laboratories with little delay. As a result, even in the two decades of uneasy armistice which followed, curtailed at both ends by the confusion of recovery from one war and the gathering menace of another, research for the normal purposes of peace was resumed with an astonishing promptitude, and the advance of knowledge surged forward with an imposing acceleration. Almost any man of science who can cast his mind back to the state of knowledge in his own special subject in 1919, and compare it with that which had been reached in 1939, must be impressed by the transformation. To mention an example which cannot be far, at the moment, from anyone's thoughts, consider the revolutionary changes made, between the wars, in our whole conception of the material universe, by new theories of atomic structure, with new apparatus of mathematics to deal with them, by experimental attack on the atomic nucleus leading to transmutation of elements and, still before war's dark curtain fell again, clear evidence of atomic fission, with the release of atomic energy. As one other example, who would have predicted in 1919 that, of the vitamins and hormones then known and differentiated only by the effects of their withdrawal and replacement, imposing ranges would have been isolated, identified, and made by artificial synthesis before 1939? And now that we are emerging from another war, into what, if we scientists can do anything to prevent it, will not be just another precarious interlude before a worse disaster, we must try to ensure that the free advancement of natural knowledge, which this Society exists to promote, is able to claim again, with as little delay as possible, the full service of its natural leaders.

Another condition of the revival of scientific activity for the normal purposes of peace, seen clearly by our predecessors in 1919, was a rapid reconstruction of the international community of science. Before there had been time for the full attainment of their aim, the forces of cleavage had again begun to operate; but, as soon as it became possible once again to think of rebuilding what another war had broken, it was the first duty of the Royal Society to ensure that use was made of all that was of proven value, in the framework of international collaboration which had been constructed between the wars. Past Officers of the Society, especially Sir Arthur Schuster and Sir Henry Lyons, had taken prominent parts in the foundation and development of this organ of international collaboration. Our Foreign Secretary, Sir Henry Tizard, now coming to the end of his term of office, was early at work preparing for its revival with the Chairmen of our National Committees, in consultation with its present General Secretary, Professor Stratton, and with such representative scientists of other countries as were accessible. Their aim was to review the past achievements and potential value of this system of the International Scientific Unions, and the possible need for its extension or modification in certain directions. Our Council's reports record the progress which has been made. While, however, the Royal Society has had a special responsibility for our national participation in this existing system, it has always welcomed any opportunity of the fullest and most friendly collaboration with any other agency for the promotion of international friendship and community of action among the scientists of different countries. The Society looks forward now to the possibility of collaborating also with any scheme or mechanism for the promotion of international relations in science, which may arise under the general Organization of the United Nations. We recognize that, through such channels, it may be possible, not only to give most valuable support to the existing Unions for international action in the various fields of scientific research, but to supplement the functions of these in many other directions in which the interests of science may yet require to be internationally organized and promoted. The Society stands ready and eager, now as ever, to work with any responsible agency for the restoration and extension of international friendship and collaboration in science.

In my address to the Society last year, I referred to the aim of building anew, and on a firm and broadening foundation, a world community in science, as "an aim worthy of our utmost effort and devotion." Can it be doubted now, after what has happened since I last addressed you, that upon our success in achieving that aim may well depend, not only the free progress of science henceforward, but even the survival of civilization? I have spoken of existing and prospective mechanisms for promoting scientific intercourse between the people of different nations. We must use and develop these to the full limit of their value, but we shall still want something which no formal mechanism can restore to us. Meetings of national representatives and delegates may, indeed, do service of great importance to science, as by framing and accepting international conventions on units of scientific measurement, or on technical terminology;

but no mechanism which merely brings scientists together as national representatives, no finding of formulae or passage of resolutions will do for science to-day what the world so desperately needs. If we are to achieve anything really to meet that need, we must somehow get rid of barriers which hinder the scientists of different countries from meeting simply as scientists, for the frank and informal interchange and friendly criticism of each others' observations and ideas, in complete freedom from any national inhibitions or restrictions. Before 1914 we were able to claim that science belonged thus to the world, knew no frontiers, was one and indivisible. Many of us had been cherishing the hope that the union of so much of the world in a war for the defence of freedom—freedom, we understood, for science as for all man's other activities—would have brought, with victory, a possibility of reviving this claim and restoring this ideal, which the intervening years had so shaken and obscured. Even a few weeks ago the trend of events did not appear to encourage that aspiration; but we may find, in the end, that it will suffer less from an open challenge, which all the world can see, than from a more gradual discouragement.

To all but a few scientists, as to the rest of the world, the use of the atomic bombs on Japanese cities brought the first news of a tremendous scientific and technical achievement, as well as the recognition of a new problem of overpowering importance to the world. Scientists might well take pride in it, as a triumphant verification of a purely scientific prediction. The main lines of this had been completed before the outbreak of war in 1939, by experimental and theoretical physicists of many countries. We think proudly here of the pioneer part which our own Rutherford with his pupils and associates had played in the opening of a new science of nuclear physics; but we recognize that its development was a widely international achievement. The practical realization in a little over three years of what these academic scientists had foreseen as a distant possibility, required a scientific and technical undertaking of a new order. It is unlikely that any stimulus other than the urgency of war would have sufficed to induce any national, or other, organization to embark upon such an enterprise. It is certain that, under the world conditions in which that stimulus was applied, the United States of America was the only country in the world where the project could have been undertaken. The result was a prodigy of organization and achievement, both scientific and technical; and though, in the nature of the case, America made the largest contribution even to the team of scientists engaged in the great volume of theoretical and experimental researches still required, we may be glad to think that, on that side, the enterprise still owed much to a widely international effort. It drew into its service a large proportion of the nuclear physicists of this country and of Canada, with others who had escaped from the clutches of the German invader in Denmark and in France, and yet others who had fled before the war from Germany, from Austria and from Italy, to conditions of freedom and new opportunity in Britain and the United States.

The enthusiasm with which the world of science would normally have received the news of an event of such magnitude in scientific history was qualified by the unique conditions of its general announcement. The world at large has not been slow to grasp the tremendous implications which it may hold for the future of civilization, and the nature of the choice with which it has so dramatically faced mankind. The problems which it has raised are clearly everybody's concern. Nevertheless, and in spite of certain threats and rumblings, I believe that general opinion will allow to us men of science, in addition to our common rights as citizens, a special claim to be heard on the uses which the world is to make of this great new gift of science to mankind. General opinion, I think, would further recognize that the many scientists who have taken a direct part in this great achievement have a special right and duty to let the world know how, in the light of their intimate and expert knowledge, they view the promise and the threat which it offers to humanity. Surely they, if any, have a right to speak; and we others can welcome the firmness and the substantial unanimity with which many of them have let their opinions be known. We have a duty, indeed, to the statesmen, who are carrying this new and heavy burden of responsibility for the world's future, and who have to deal with aspects of the problem in which science is not directly concerned. It is a part of that duty, however, to keep them in touch with the general body of opinion, among the scientists of the free peoples whom they represent, so that in framing their policy they may be confident that the service

required of science to make it effective will be given with enthusiasm and conviction, and not, if at all, with a reluctant
acquiescence. Most, if not all of you, will have read words
which our Prime Minister spoke to the Canadian Parliament,
and emphasized by repeating them to our own House of Commons a week ago. This is what Mr Attlee said: "Unless we apply
to the solution of these problems a moral enthusiasm as great as
that which scientists bring to their research work, then our
civilization, built up over so many centuries, will surely perish."
I do not doubt that you will share my glow of gratitude for a
tribute which we must try to deserve.

It is not fitting that I should discuss from this Chair matters
which belong to a much wider constituency than ours, and my
particular purpose to-day is to ask you to consider an aspect of
this world problem, which is, beyond challenge, our special
concern as men of science—the effect of present and prospective
developments upon the integrity of science itself. Will any
deny our claim to hold that as a sacred trust for the world, and
to be alert to defend it from any danger which may seem to
threaten it? I believe that we have a duty to be watchful now
against a serious danger to it from the intrusion of secrecy, which
we know here from long tradition and experience to be alien to
the spirit of science as we have known and cherished it. I cannot
claim the time which would be required to deal adequately with
such a theme. Permit me, however, to bring certain aspects of
it briefly to your notice, without attempt at full or ordered
discussion.

1. This danger, of course, has not newly arisen with the
explosion of the first atomic bomb. We have known it long in
connexion with the use of scientific research by industry, and
with the relatively minor and accessory part played, till recently,
by science in preparing the apparatus of war. Even in those
connexions, there was a growing recognition of the detrimental
effect of secrecy on the relations between the scientists concerned
and the general scientific community, and a consequent effort to
reduce its applications to the minimum which industrial or
military opinion would accept.

2. The real and growing danger arises, however, from the new
conception of war, due to the breach and consequent abandonment, in rapid succession, of conventions and restrictions which,

not long ago, seemed permanent and sacred. Thus by the end of this recent war, step by step, with Germany always leading, the combatant nations had come to regard, as a proper war aim, not merely the winning of mastery over the enemy's fighting forces, but the compulsion of his surrender by indiscriminate destruction, by any means, of his people and their possessions. This principle of 'total war,' as we learned too easily from our enemies to call it, having once been accepted, science found itself, no longer a mere accessory of military action, but increasingly a central agent, a direct combatant, and the provider of a limitless vista of destructive possibilities. Last year I spoke of the warning of such developments which the German V weapons had given, and the dropping of the first atomic bombs has now given to that warning a new and sterner emphasis.

3. Preparation by our enemies for the use of science in such total war, and our own for defence against it by reprisal, have alike involved the binding of a nation's scientific effort to secrecy on a scale beyond all earlier experience. This we accepted readily, with so much else, as a necessity of war. The freedom of science, as of all that made life worth living, was at stake; if by submitting for a while to secrecy we could help to save that freedom and to establish it for ever, we could not hesitate; but we must be watchful now against any easy assumption that that submission will be continued into peace.

4. As has now been recognized by international pronouncement, it cannot be assumed that the atomic bomb, or any contrivance using the release of atomic energy, represents the only direction, or even of necessity the most effective one, in which science could be perverted to the purposes of this "total war," as a direct agent for the destruction of one people by another, or of dominance by the threat of it. The atomic bomb has given immediate prominence to the problem, but the world might have had to face it, even if the attempt to release atomic energy had failed, or had never been made. The nations, in fact, have now to decide how they intend to use the powers and the resources which science stands ready to offer in growing abundance. Will they let science work again and henceforward in freedom, once more as an international community, and use what it offers for the raising of all mankind to levels of material prosperity and of culture above any that we can picture? Or will they try still

to bind science to secrecy, for the competitive invention of ever more effective means of destruction, and thus hold civilization in instant peril of dissolution? It is surely our duty as men of science to help the world with our knowledge to make that decision, and to make clear our own views and intentions.

5. The danger to science from the intrusion of secrecy, against which I suggest that we need to be alert, does not arise, of course, simply from the question whether a particular technical invention shall be given away at once, or not till somebody else has made it. If policies now developing can bring about a frank and effective abandonment of all national secrecy about science, we need not, as scientists, be critical of their beginnings. Our experience so far, however, of the application of secrecy to science for military or industrial advantage, must keep us on guard. It has not, in our experience hitherto, dealt with inventions which can, once for all, be locked up or given away. The most that it has hoped to achieve has been to keep its particular employer, at each new stage, a jump ahead of his rivals. What we have now to fear is that, in default of the international agreement which we must hope and work for, national military secrecy should try to maintain, or to extend, its war-time dominance. If that were to happen, we must expect it, with its new experience of the possibilities of science in total war, to be watchful for any advance, whether fundamental or technical, whether in nuclear physics or in any other progressive field of science, which could be impounded and put under seal for warlike preparation, presumably under the name of "security." It is impossible to forecast how much of science might thus become involved. The release of atomic energy is yet a novelty, and we have to think what might be made of it, for good or ill, twenty, thirty, or forty years ahead. I think that we, as scientists, should make it clear to the world that, if national military secrecy were allowed thus progressively to encroach upon the freedom of science, even if civilization should yet for a while escape the danger of final destruction, a terrible, possibly a mortal wound would have been inflicted on the free spirit of science itself, to the immeasurable loss of what it stands ready to offer to a wiser world.

6. I do not believe that there is any division of opinion on this issue among scientists, anywhere in the world, in so far as they are able to express it simply as scientists. We of the United

Nations, in despite of all our normal traditions and instincts, were ready to submit for years to any secrecy or restriction which could help or hasten victory in the war for the world's freedom. The war has been won, and we shall not be ready to accept, as its result for science, a tightening of the chains. We have the right to expect that its freedom will be restored; and the freedoms which we ask for science are freedom from secrecy and freedom from national barriers.

7. Secrecy as the enemy, and resistance to the attempt of authority to impose it, are no new experiences for science or for scientists. Giordano Bruno was burned at the stake and Galileo was imprisoned and threatened, because they refused to be secret about discoveries which were thought to be harmful to religion in their day; and, in a later century, there was an attempt, for a like reason, to discourage scientists by moral ostracism from telling the truth as they had seen and discovered it. Science stood firm, the world still moved, the moral stature of mankind was raised by the encounter, and organized religion gained more from it in wisdom than it lost in intellectual dominance. We do not know yet who, or how many, of Europe's scientists, in the terrible years now closing, have suffered for the scientific truths which political tyrannies desired to suppress or to distort. Unless the growth of international understanding and confidence can now prevent it, unless efforts to outlaw the abuse of science for "total war" should succeed, science may find itself again facing an attempt to impose secrecy upon it, this time in the interests of national suspicion and rivalry, and in flat negation of its true service to mankind. If that danger should threaten, can we hope that the scientists of all the world may yet stand together against it, determined to preserve the integrity of science, to prevent its further perversion from its proper and beneficent uses, and to save civilization from misusing science for its own destruction?

Our Charter of 1663 lays down, as the object of our Society, "promoting by the authority of experiments the sciences of natural things and of useful arts, to the glory of God the Creator, and the advantage of the human race." Each of us may read these old words to-day in terms of his personal convictions. Freely to seek "by the authority of experiments" and freely to proclaim the truth as science reveals it, for its own beauty and excellence

THE SILVER JUBILEE OF
INSULIN 1946*

WE MEET to commemorate the Silver Jubilee of an event which, as it seems to me, has formed a turning-point in the recent history of medical knowledge won by experiment, and of its application for the relief of human ailments. Most of those present have an additional and personal reason for remembering a scientific triumph so directly concerned with the possibility of their being here at all, to take part in this little celebration. It is now just over twenty-five years since two young Canadians, with practically no previous experience of scientific research in any field, boldly embarked upon a quest for a prize which had eluded all who had earlier sought it, and many of whom had been men of ripe scientific attainment. Their quest was for a method of obtaining from the pancreas, in a form which would allow it to be kept long enough and purified sufficiently for practical use, a principle long postulated by theory but, till then, resisting all attempts even to prove its existence by direct evidence. We are here to recall the fact that, in a few devoted months of work through the heat of the Canadian summer of 1921, these two young enthusiasts were able to see the prize and to grasp it, for science and for suffering humanity. They were able not only to establish the existence of the long-sought "insulin"—the natural principle, or hormone, missing from the diabetic body's chemical equipment—but even to prepare it in sufficient quantity for practical trial.

In recalling that achievement of a quarter of a century ago, we remember also the early death by accident, on a mission of wartime duty twenty years later, of Frederick Grant Banting, the senior of those two young pioneers, and the one whose vision and insistence, rejecting all conventional warning and discouragement, led them so directly to the goal, and to the triumph which we are here to commemorate. I know, too, that you will wish me to say,

---

* Banting Memorial Lecture delivered to the Diabetic Association, Silver Jubilee Meeting at the Royal Institution, 21 Albemarle St., London W.1, on 5th July 1946.

on behalf of all of you, with what joy we welcome the personal presence of Charles Best, Fred Banting's younger partner, here to-day to help us to recall what happened twenty-five years ago, and to salute with us the memory of his leader and comrade in that epic enterprise.

To obtain a clearer impression of the meaning of what happened in 1921, let me remind you in a little more detail of the position at that date, and of the stages by which it had been reached. More than thirty years earlier, in 1889, Minkowski, in Strassburg, having removed the pancreas from a dog for the purpose of an entirely different enquiry, had come by accident upon the fact that this operation caused a condition corresponding in practically all respects to the severest kind of diabetes. We should remember that the first successful replacement by administration of what we should now call a missing hormone, was then still in the future. I remember the news of it five years later, in 1894, just at the beginning of my student days at Cambridge*. Minkowski's observation, accordingly, lay widely open to speculative interpretation. It might mean, indeed, that some principle was produced by the pancreas which was needed to maintain the normal balance between the supply and storage of glucose, and the body's demand for it. On the other hand, it might mean, with equal likelihood, that the normal pancreas had the function of destroying some poisonous by-product of the vital chemistry, which would upset this delicate sugar-balance, if it were allowed to persist. If the function of the pancreas were of this latter kind, it would clearly be useless to administer anything extracted from it, in the hope of making good the diabetic defect; and, as we have seen, for more than thirty years, all attempts to extract such a remedial agent had failed, so that it remained a still open question, whether it existed at all, or, if it existed, was ever present in sufficient amount to be extracted.

Evidence of another kind, originating with the microscopical study of its origin, had tended to influence opinion in those intervening years in favour of the production of a hormone by the pancreas, and against its action as the destructor of a poison; though logically the evidence in question had done no more than

---

* This, no doubt, was literally true. The first successful hormone treatment, of myxoedema with thyroid gland, took place in 1891; but there is no reason why I should have heard about it till 1894.

to point to a particular tissue of the pancreas as responsible for maintaining the sugar-balance and preventing diabetes, by either of these methods. Twenty years before Minkowski's discovery, in 1869, one Langerhans had presented, as his inaugural dissertation to the University of Berlin, a description of certain nests or islands of cells in the pancreas, having no apparent connexion with the ordinary glandular tissue which secreted the digestive juice into the bowel. Just to identify them, it became customary to refer to these structures as "islets of Langerhans"; and the place in medical history which the name thus acquired has now been additionally assured, by the fact that the discovery of insulin has brought these islets to the notice of millions who had otherwise been unlikely ever to hear of them, or of the young man who first described them. When the implication of Minkowski's discovery came to be fully recognized and discussed, the suggestion became current that the islets might be the part of the pancreas specially concerned with controlling the production and use of sugar in the body, and a further suggestion that they did this by the internal secretion of a hormone. This idea was most clearly formulated in 1899 by Diamare in Italy and Schäfer, known to many of us later as Sir Edward Sharpey-Schafer, in this country. Schäfer thought so well of it that he even proposed the name "insulin" for this hormone from the islets, the very existence of which was, so far, purely a matter of inference. Of special importance for its effect on Banting was the observation made by Schiff, Hédon, and others that blocking the duct of the pancreas caused its ordinary, secreting tissue to disappear, leaving only islets of Langerhans surviving, but causing no diabetes; and Hédon's finding that even the grafting of such an islet-containing remnant of pancreatic tissue under the skin sufficed to prevent diabetes, when the rest of the pancreas was removed.

It will be seen, however, that in all this there was nothing really decisive for the production of a regulating hormone rather than the destruction of an interfering poison; all that the evidence really showed was, that whichever of these functions was performed by the pancreas as a whole was performed by the islets alone, when the rest of the gland had disappeared.

And meanwhile experimenters had published accounts of their unsuccessful attempts to extract the suggested but elusive hormone from the pancreas, and others continued to do so in the two decades which followed; and I think that we may safely assume that others, perhaps many others, had tried, without leaving any record of their defeats. In the light of what is now known it is not easy to find a complete explanation for the failure of all these efforts; for some of them seem to have followed lines which departed little, if at all, from those which eventually led to success. It is not unlikely that investigators of experience, well versed in the history of frustration which stretched behind their attempts, were too easily discouraged; so that one who had, in fact, extracted insulin would fail to demonstrate its presence for lack of an additional step needed to rid his extract of antagonistic concomitants, while another would hastily attribute symptoms, actually due to overdosage with insulin, to an extraneous and irrelevant toxicity; and both would abandon the effort. Too much experience, in such cases, might hinder the pursuit of the quarry with the essential tenacity of conviction.

It should be remembered, too, that in 1921 the pancreas was not alone in this failure of attempts to extract its hormone. There were many other cases in which characteristic effects were known to follow removal of an organ, and to be prevented by grafts of its tissue, in which similar failures to make active extracts had become a matter of common experience. Only two among such glands, indeed, the thyroid and the suprarenal medulla, had yet yielded recognizable hormones to extraction*. It was easy to suppose, then, that the hormones of others, and of the pancreas among them, if they existed at all, were formed in their respective glands at rates which only kept pace with the body's needs for them, so that there was never any excess to be stored and extracted. It was equally easy to suppose, on the other hand, that they were all too sensitive to be extracted and handled in artificial media, and that adrenaline and thyroxine were exceptional in their tolerance of such rough treatment.

Banting, with his unblunted enthusiasm and courageous

---

* It is rather remarkable that I seem to have forgotten, in this connexion, the active substances so readily extractable from the posterior pituitary lobe—the one chapter of endocrinology to which I had myself made a positive contribution. And my failure is particularly curious, in view of the fact that such an extract had already been in use, for a good many years before insulin, for the successful control of the much rarer and less serious form of diabetes, due to a deficiency of this pituitary lobe, and known as *diabetes insipidus*.

enterprise, was to sweep like a fresh breeze into this atmosphere of discouragement and scepticism. There was nothing in his training or his record, so far, to suggest that he might succeed where so many had failed, or to account for the sudden decision, backed by a reckless determination, which was to change his whole career, and life's prospect for so many. With sound farming ancestry and country schooling in Ontario, he had had a normal medical student's career at Toronto, till the war of 1914 broke into it. Banting enlisted and saw service as a private in the Canadian Army Medical Corps; but he was sent home to finish his quali-fication, returned to France with a commission, won a Military Cross for conspicuous bravery, and was so badly wounded that he only just escaped amputation of an arm. What would he have achieved, if he had lost it? Not, we may be certain, what has brought us here to-day. Army experience seems to have given surgery, and orthopaedics in particular, a prior place in his interests. Banting had a craftsman's hands and an artist's vision; records which he was later to leave from his holidays, made without special training, were to show what he might have achieved as a painter of the glories of Canada's landscape, if accident or impulse had shaped his career in that direction. At the time when he had finished his resident appointments in Toronto, however, nobody would have credited him with more than just the kind of com-petence and experience which would make him a good practical doctor, with a leaning towards surgery; and in that capacity he began to practise in London, Ontario, in 1920, at the age of 29. He had plans for marriage, had taken a house and was furnishing it; everything seemed set for a normal and useful, if not specially distinguished, career in the provincial practice of medicine. Meanwhile, as the practice was growing slowly, he had accepted part-time duty as a demonstrator of physiology in the University. It was certainly in that connexion that he came upon the idea which provided the starting-point for the work on insulin; but this, by itself, gives us no real clue to the urgency which made Banting suddenly change his whole plan of life to follow it. He was, apparently, preparing a lecture on diabetes, and we may suppose that the evidence concerning the function of the pancreas would come to his notice with more freshness of interest than to most teachers of physiology. He was seized with the idea that the failures to find insulin in the gland had been due to its destruction by the powerful protein-digesting ferment, liberated from the cells of the normal pancreas in the process of extraction. Thence came the idea that, if the cells producing the ferment were made to degenerate by blocking the duct, insulin might be extracted from the islets, known to be left in the shrunken remnant of such a gland. The idea was good enough in itself, and there was nothing on record to suggest that it had been tried before. Even if it had, the years then recent had seen advances in methods of analysis, such as those for measuring the sugar in blood, which would have made it worth trial anew. We cannot suppose, however, that the project presented itself to Banting in a form so qualified. For reasons which will always elude our probing, it came to him with the blaze of a sudden illumination, as a call to action so urgent, a mission so imperative, that no sacrifice was too great to follow it. Nothing must stand in the way. He divested himself of his practice, of house and furniture, and off he went to Toronto to find the opportunity to put the idea to the test of experiment, hoping that his means would last long enough to let him finish the job.

I find myself in sympathy with what is reported of the late Professor McLeod's reaction to the approach of this wild enthusiast. While agreeing to give Banting the accommodation which he required for the trial, he is said to have warned him against expecting any easy success in what so many men of long experience had attempted in vain. I hope, though without any clear conviction, that, if I had been faced with McLeod's problem, I should not have been more discouraging. And we ought not to forget that, whatever friendly warning he may have felt it his duty to give, McLeod not only gave Banting the place and the opportunity for which he asked; he did him a further and inestimable service, in making it clear that Banting's equipment for his mission, which amounted then to little beyond a competent surgical technique, would need to be reinforced by the coöperation of somebody well trained in the latest methods of biochemical analysis, if the proposed investigation was to have any hope of success. It was thus that one of McLeod's recent pupils, Charles Best, still a medically ungraduated student, was chosen to join with Banting in what was to be an historic partnership. At first Banting supplied the surgery, while Best made the determinations of sugar in blood and urine and of respiratory quotients; but each taught the other, and soon they were fully sharing all the exacting details of the daily and hourly task, as well as the eagerness and the excitement. They told us later how, on occasion, they had taken turns at watching and sleeping, when, through forty-eight hours on end of summer heat, an experiment demanded unbroken vigil and hourly analyses, if all its harvest of evidence was to be gathered. And then, after a few months of this concentrated labour, the first results began to come clear. "The intense excitement and pleasure," writes Best, "with which we watched the depth of colour in the sugar reagent fade, as the blood sugar of the diabetic animals became reduced under the action of insulin, is difficult to describe." These first clear results, obtained with extracts from a pancreas brought to degeneration by blockage of its duct, must have meant for Banting, especially, a triumphant vindication of the idea for which he had forsaken all prospects, and which he had pursued with such intensity of conviction. They proceeded to make extracts of foetal pancreas, in order to catch the islets and extract insulin from them, before the digestive enzymes appeared in the developing gland. And then, by the autumn of 1921, it had become clear that, with suitable methods of extraction and some fractionation of the product to free it from interfering concomitants, insulin could be obtained from the ordinary adult pancreas of beasts slaughtered for food, and the prospect of its practical use in medicine came clearly into view.

The quest for insulin thus passed from the phase of a scientific adventure to that of an urgent race for the relief of a human need. For the best speed of advance, more hands than those of the joint discoverers were required, and, under Professor McLeod's lead and stimulus, other workers were called in to accelerate progress. Among a number of these, J. B. Collip, now a well-known Professor in Montreal, should be specially mentioned. It would lead far beyond the scope of my purpose to-day to speak in any detail of the rapid development which followed. As a landmark in its progress I may mention the discovery that insulin will cause the sugar in the blood of healthy animals to fall below its normal level, so that it can be measured by the effects which it produces on normal rabbits or mice. This had a most important effect on the rate of progress, enabling the further development of knowledge about insulin to spread widely through the laboratories of the world.

I first met Banting, Best, and others of the Toronto team who, by then, were taking a hand in the practical problem of producing insulin for use, when I was sent over in September, 1922, by the Medical Research Council, with my late colleague, Harold Dudley, to get news at first hand of the great discovery which was just beginning to be applied in practice. Banting, by that time, had clearly decided that such further developments in the laboratory required chemical knowledge and technique beyond his compass. He had transferred his interest largely to the clinic, and he gave me the privilege of visiting with him some of the earliest patients to be rescued, by the use even of the crude insulin which was then available. I received a strong impression that the dominant motive with Banting, the force behind the ruthless determination with which he had driven himself towards the goal, had been the desire to be directly concerned with the saving of human life and the relief of a human need. He was essentially, I gathered, a doer rather than a thinker—a man unlikely to be much interested in any theory, unless it showed a more direct way to new medical knowledge which could be applied in practice.

My first inclination, when I met Banting, was to think that the best reward that could be given him for what he had achieved, would be freedom for some years of quiet study, to fill in the gaps which the war and other accidents of his student career had left in his scientific background; so that he might later be able to give rein to his fine instinct for research with more confidence in his general equipment. Later thoughts, however, made me doubt whether such a policy would have been right, or effective. To ask Banting to contribute to a general structure of scientific knowledge growing slowly and surely, "creeping on from point to point," with faith in some far-off use for the easing of human ills, would, I suspect, have been to misuse his best qualities of enthusiasm and spontaneity, his natural instinct to drive straight for a practical issue. The repute of his achievement, first in his own country and spreading thence round the world, soon created an atmosphere which would have made it practically impossible, in any case, for Banting to subside into the role of a patient participant in a general advance. Patience was not his particular virtue; if it had been, there are some present to-night who would probably not have been here; and when press agents are following a man's

every movement about the world and eavesdropping to gather
hot news of new discoveries from his casual conversation, it
cannot be easy for him, whatever his temperament, to settle down
to the steady production and publication of sound, but unsensa-
tional, additions to knowledge. Banting was soon ready, therefore, to leave the insulin field of enquiry to others. He had little
part in the further developments which so rapidly led to its
large-scale production as a pure-crystalline salt, and in the further
studies on the mechanism and significance of its physiological
action. His instinct was for further swift and direct attacks on
other problems which had baffled earlier attempts to solve them.
He worked thus for successive periods on the adrenal cortex and
on transmissible malignant tumours, getting results which, from
an ordinary worker, would have been regarded as sufficiently
interesting; but there was nothing here, as in the work on insulin,
to change the whole aspect of knowledge of a disease, or the
prospect of those whom it afflicted. Of the other campaigns on
which he thus embarked, the one which at present seems most
likely to produce results of permanent value for human health is
that in which he attacked the problem of silicosis.

In any case it is for insulin that Banting will be longest and
most gratefully remembered, and rightly so. We are unlikely
here to undervalue that discovery for its own sake, but I think
that, in full justice to Banting's memory, we ought also to take
note of its stimulating effect over a much wider field of knowledge. I have spoken of the air of discouragement and scepticism
concerning the pancreatic hormone, which only such reckless
enthusiasm as Banting's could dissipate. Much the same attitude
prevailed, at the same date, with regard to most of the hormones
which, on indirect evidence, had been attributed to other glands;
and, although Banting himself had no direct success with these,
I am sure that the successful attack on the pancreas, which he had
led with such conviction, had the effect of a tremendous stimulus
and encouragement to others who, in due course, were to succeed
in extracting hormones from the parathyroid gland, the gonads,
the suprarenal cortex, the liver, and in varied series from the
anterior pituitary lobe, which Langdon-Brown has so
picturesquely termed "the conductor of the endocrine orchestra."
Nor, I think, did the effect of the stimulus end there. Not only
were there many hormones, in 1921, concerning which it was

reasonable then to doubt whether they were sufficiently stable, or stored in sufficient abundance, to enable them ever to be isolated and characterized; doubts of a similar kind seemed then to be justified concerning all the vitamins known at that time. Yet, even in the short remainder of that uneasy interval between two wars, whole ranges of both hormones and vitamins were to be not merely isolated and characterized, but even prepared by artificial synthesis. Of course there were other factors of importance in this astonishing transformation; one was the elucidation of the general structure of the steroids, to which group so many of the more recently isolated hormones were found to belong, as well as the vitamin D. Nevertheless, whatever may have been the causes contributory to the later acceleration of this change, when we try to follow it back to its point of origin, to the first spark which fired the train, I think that I am not wrong in tracing it to Banting's attack on the problem of the pancreas and insulin. The success of this, it seems to me, achieved much more, then, than its immediate and consciously chosen objective. It put new heart into inquiry over a much wider field, attracting into it new workers, fired with a spirit of fresh hope and enterprise. Thus other conditions of endocrine deficiency which, like diabetes, had long been regarded as probably for ever beyond the reach of relief, came one after another under effective treatment.

Fred Banting was only fifty years old when his life was ended by a tragic accident in 1941, on a journey undertaken to organize the wartime coöperation in medical research between Canada and Britain, his own land and its mother, which he had loved and served with a characteristically fierce devotion. He would not have shirked such a fate if he could have seen it coming, and I believe that he would have been glad to think that we should here remember that he died in serving the British Empire, at the time of its peril and its need. Some of us here can cherish the memory of our friend Fred Banting as a man—a man who was simple and direct in his character and his habits of thought, readily moved to strong enthusiasms and, on occasion, to strong and not always reasonable resentments; one who was always eager to act for the relief of human illness and suffering, and who responded with a special tenderness to the appeal of a sick child. The world at large will remember him, and he would have desired to be first remembered, as the young doctor who, now twenty-five years ago, put behind him all other hopes and prospects, and went forward with a clear conviction, which no warnings of experience could weaken or deflect, to win the knowledge which has given new health and activity to a growing multitude of those who, without it, would have had no prospect but a few years of misery and privation. Let us remember him so, and remember also that, without the stimulus and the encouragement which came from Frederick Banting's achievement, the world might have had to wait much longer for other gains of knowledge already in use for the healing of mankind, and for yet others, perhaps, which are still to be won.

THE FREEDOM OF SCIENCE*

IN thanking the National Academy of Sciences of Washington for the invitation to give this, the sixth of the Pilgrim Trust Lectures, may I be allowed to say a word about the origin of the series, which it concludes? The idea first took shape in London in the summer of 1937, in conversation between your Foreign Secretary at that time, known almost as well in England and in France as in his own country, the late Lawrence J. Henderson, and a secretary of the Royal Society of London, A. V. Hill. I heard of the plan from Professors Henderson and Hill as we dined together at that time, and of the proposal to appeal for financial support to the Pilgrim Trust, administering a great American endowment for the benefit of Britain. The generous offer, made by the Trust in response, was gladly accepted by your Academy and by the Royal Society. The series of six annual lectures for which it provided started in 1938, but it has been spread over eight years by the events which have intervened.

The promoters of the scheme were among those who still preserved the hope of rebuilding a truly international community in science. Memory had preserved from happier times experience of such a community as a substantial reality, though it had been impossible to ignore a weakening of its influence by national rivalries and resentments, even before it was rudely shattered by the outbreak of war in Europe in 1914. The effort to reopen, after 1918, the channels which had thus been broken, to recreate the feeling of confidence and common interest among the scientists of different countries, though it encountered natural difficulties from the hatreds and suspicions which such a war leaves in its train, had been able to claim a steady advance towards its objective until, from 1933 onwards, the open resurgence of aggressive nationalism had made the threat of war loom large again. And it was clear already that, if this could not be averted, it would be a war diverting science from its proper aim and using its powers for destruction to an extent beyond all earlier experience.

---

* Pilgrim Trust Lecture, read 22nd October, 1946, in Philadelphia before the National Academy of Sciences.

By 1937 this drift to a new disaster for the world and its peoples had become ominously clear; and I believe that those in our two countries who, at that juncture, were concerned to promote and to accept this scheme of alternating invitations to lecture, were not without hope that something more widely international might ultimately come of such a friendly exchange, though immediately it could only strengthen ties of international fellowship where these had always been easiest to maintain, because of the common heritage of a mother-tongue and of so much of earlier history and tradition. Even this, perhaps, might help to keep alive, and ready for a new emergence when the time should be more propitious, that full and inclusive understanding and confidence among scientists of all nations, which had once seemed so natural, but which, in 1937, was fading again from view with such a menacing rapidity.

Dr. Langmuir and the late Sir William Bragg gave the first two lectures of this series before war broke out. Then illness and, later, his much lamented death frustrated the plans which Professor Lawrence Henderson had made so eagerly to come to London for the third. By the time that Dr. Karl Compton came, in 1943, all the scientific resources of both our countries had been turned to a largely coöperative service of the war, and his lecture naturally dealt with America's great organization to that end. Professor Adrian, lecturing here in 1944, when it began to be possible to foresee the end, and Professor Muller in London last year, when Japan's surrender had already brought an end to hostilities, were able to return for their subjects to the normal scientific interests and activities of peace. It might have been thought, then, that I should be able to do this even more freely to-day. I most heartily wish that it could have been so; but there are questions now facing us all, as scientists, which have a greater urgency than any special problem or line of research. Dr. Muller, indeed, had hardly left England when you invited me to come here last November, to give this lecture, as an item of a symposium you were holding then with the American Philosophical Society of Philadelphia, to discuss the freedom of science and its international relations. I was bound by duties in London then; but you honoured me by renewing the invitation now, when you have further extended the circle and given the discussion of such broad problems and interests of science a more widely international basis, by inviting representative scientists of many nations to take part. The meeting is still in progress, but it is possible to welcome already the evidence which it has given of a general desire among the men of science of the nations here represented to resume the fullest possible coöperation; evidence also, which a number of the individual communications have given, of the recognition that there are wide areas of scientific activity in which the most complete international collaboration is urgently needed and, most happily, should be possible now without further delay.

At the same time we must recognize the disappointment of any hope which we may have entertained of a disappearance, by now, of the doubts and anxieties for the future of science itself which troubled us a year ago, though we have not been left without encouragement. Scientists throughout the world, so far as it has been possible to make touch with them, have made it abundantly clear that they recognize, and passionately desire to see removed, the danger with which the war's legacy of world policies threatens the freedom and the prospect of science, and the kindred danger with which the perversion of science threatens the future of the world. It would be an unpardonable abuse of the privilege which you have given me if I were to intrude upon the sphere of international politics on such an occasion. We scientists have our individual duties to advocate or to criticize the plans under discussion at those high levels of tremendous responsibility, for the prevention of dangers which, with our fellow citizens of the world, we apprehend. It is not to be expected that we shall be completely unanimous in our judgments of such matters; but we have, of course, the special duty of ensuring that decisions, which may mean so much for the future of mankind, are taken in the light of all that science can provide of precise knowledge and sound prediction. A peril to the world's civilization is the affair of all the world's citizens, ourselves among them. A peril to science should also be the concern of all the world; but nobody will deny that that is our special responsibility as men of science. Nobody can question our particular duty to consider whether anything can be done to rescue science, and therewith civilization, from a danger which threatens both. If it is the general belief of this assembly, as it is mine, that nothing could so much conduce to that end as a renewal of the full and intimate confidence and community of interest among the scientists of all the world; of that informal brotherhood in science, ignoring all national and political frontiers and all differences of social philosophy, which effectively existed within the memory of so many of us—if that is our belief, then it is clearly our first and imperative duty to consider whether anything stands in the way of such a renewal, and, if so, whether we can do anything to remove it.

I assume that there will be no lack of agreement among us in repudiating any suggestion that science itself is to be held responsible for the problems and the danger with which the world is faced, or that science should be halted or retarded in its progress, in order to enable the moral and political enlightenment of mankind to overtake the changing situation. Such a principle of action would have brought the advance of civilization to a standstill at the point where our remote and primitive ancestors made the first, perhaps, of all scientific discoveries, in the production of fire. Presented thus with an agent most powerful for his advance from savagery to culture, or, if otherwise used, for the destruction at any time of all that his race had achieved in that advance, man had succeeded in turning and developing its uses, more and more through the ages, to creative and beneficent ends. And now, in these recent years of war, fire has again been unleashed for destruction, on a scale far beyond anything that our half-civilized predecessors would have dared to contemplate. The world and science itself are threatened, then, not because science is advancing too fast, but because mankind has recklessly abandoned moral standards which had been won by painful striving and gathered wisdom through the centuries, and which had enabled it for so long to use the gifts of science with growing safety. It may be worth while to consider briefly how this has come about.

While we may all agree with Benjamin Franklin's opinion that "there never was a good war or a bad peace," it will also be accepted, I think, that, up to the outbreak of the First World War in 1914, there had been a continuous effort to limit by agreement, even for the combatants, the sufferings inflicted by war, and to secure for civilians the fullest possible immunity from its dangers. I like, in that connection, to remember Sir John Pringle, who was Physician-General to the British Army in

Flanders in 1744, and, in that capacity, is credited with the initiative which led opposing armies first to recognize the right of the medical services, and of the wounded under their care, to be free from attack. If you will pardon a momentary digression, it was the same Sir John Pringle who, as President of the Royal Society from 1772 to 1778, became involved in a famous controversy about Benjamin Franklin's lightning-conductors, concerning which one Benjamin Wilson had argued that their ends ought to be round, not pointed. The Royal Society being asked by the Government for its opinion, referred the question to a Committee, of which Henry Cavendish and Joseph Priestley were among the members, and this Committee gave complete support to Franklin in its conclusions. When Pringle as president reported this to King George III in 1777, that obstinate monarch, inclined by then to view with disfavour any of Dr. Franklin's activities, endeavoured to persuade Pringle to abandon his Committee and to support Franklin's opponent. Pringle protested his dutiful desire to serve the King to the limit of his powers; "but, Sire," said he, "I cannot reverse the laws and operations of nature." Perhaps, after all, to remember that the man who first propounded the principle of the Red Cross was also a staunch defender of the freedom of scientific truth from political pressure is not so irrelevant, at a time when neither of these historic immunities appears to have quite the authority which the world till recently accorded to both.

Do you remember how military activity, up to the outbreak of the war in 1914, had become circumscribed and restricted by conventions which, if not wholly logical or consistent, were at least merciful in their intention? Do you remember when that war had begun how each side accused the other of using expanding bullets, and how horrified we were by the first sinking of a merchant ship without provision for the safety of its crew? What has happened, then, to cause so rapid a lapse from the international attitude which such embargoes typified, that, by the end of the recent hostilities, nearly all humane restrictions had gone by the board, and the nations concerned had been forced, in practice if not in theory, to accept from our enemies the principle of belligerent action which they had called "total war"? In negation of all former immunities and distinctions, this conception regards the whole of a country's population,

with all its equipment for manufacture and transport, as potentially concerned with armament and maintenance for war, so
that they may be made, and have been made, the primary object
of attack. In the more recent phases of its development, indeed,
this total war has been evolving weapons of such range and such
lack of discrimination that their attack neither spares nor can
spare any part of the general life and activities of a nation, neither
the treasured monuments of its art and its history, nor any of its
hardly won and patiently built equipment for civilized existence.
The old convention, in fact, is not merely being abandoned; it
is even in danger of becoming reversed; so that war with these
new, unselective weapons may eventually come to mean that
only the non-combatant population is exposed to attack, and
only the armed forces, concerned with the release of these engines
of annihilation, are effectively protected. And this change
concerns us, not only as world citizens, but most intimately as
scientists; for such developments have only been made possible
by the full conscription for warlike uses of our science, with all
its potentially beneficent resources of knowledge, discovery,
and invention. It is surely then of the most urgent interest for
us to inquire how it has come about, and when it began.

Though it may be difficult to recognize and to disentangle all
the causes of such a decadence, I think that we may at least identify
a point of its proximate origin in the first employment of poisonous gas as a wholesale weapon in 1915. I am aware that apologists
have made a case, not implausible in itself, for regarding this
chemical warfare, especially in its later and most effective developments, as having been less cruel even than some of the weapons
which had long been recognized as normal and legitimate, in
that it killed or permanently disabled relatively few of the many
whom it put for the time out of action. I hold, none the less,
that the horror and indignation which its first employment evoked,
not least among scientists, were justified, not only because it
involved a prepared and deliberate breach of an accepted convention, but because it was recognized, half-consciously perhaps,
as a first use of science itself as a weapon, unselective in attack
and involving little or no personal risk for those charged with
its release. War, till then, however cruel its consequences, had
still been essentially a combat calling for fine qualities of manhood.
The services which science, in certain of its applications, had thus

far been called upon to render to warfare, had been concerned predominantly with the better armament and protection of personal skill and courage. Nor can anyone suggest, with records before us from the recent war as fine as any that history can show, that personal heroism and sacrifice have yet ceased to be factors, often decisive ones, in warfare as we have known it hitherto. That proud recognition, however, must not blind us to the threat, not even a distant threat, of a warfare in which personal combat between brave men has been superseded by a competition in scientific slaughter and destruction at long range. And it seems to me that those who had a clear vision of its significance might have foreseen such a development, when the first use was made of science as a weapon and a combatant in itself, with the first gas attack in 1915. We should note, also, that nobody could charge this innovation to a dangerously rapid progress of science; for the first poisons thus to be released were old and familiar chemicals, and the only real novelty was in their use for such a purpose.

When once, however, the dam of convention had thus been breached, science inevitably found itself called upon to make discoveries and inventions with the deliberate object of such misuse; and the Second World War, with science completely enrolled for such purposes by all the belligerents, was to witness a blurring and, eventually, a practical disappearance of the distinction between combatant and civilian. Thus, with the contribution of science and technology to warfare ever more in the foreground, there was rapid progress, through massed bombardment and fire-spreading from the air, pilotless planes and rocket bombs, to the use in a weapon of the enormous energy released by nuclear fission in a chain-reaction. The effect of this last, as we know, was devastation on a scale beyond previous experience, and the remoter consequences for its victims are still not fully evaluated.

It was to be expected that the sudden news of an event of such magnitude, with the knowledge that it was the first result of a vast scientific and technical enterprise, planned, undertaken, and completed under the impenetrable secrecy of war, would give a staggering shock to the opinion of an astonished world. There was indeed a brusque awakening to new apprehension of the kind of disaster in which civilization might well find itself involved by a total war thus using all the resources which science and technology could provide. I think that it was also generally understood, though not perhaps with such a vivid awareness, that the accomplished fact of the release of nuclear energy on a great scale, attained by realizing conditions which physical theorists had been able to predict with such convincing accuracy, ought, in a wiser world, to open a new era in man's mastery of nature and its powers for the common good. It was difficult to know with what past discoveries this new achievement should be compared, in respect of such beneficent promise—with that of electro-magnetic induction, perhaps, or of the use of steam for power, or of chemical combination as a source of free energy, when primitive man kindled his first fire. With this confusing contrast and competition of hopes and fears, it is no matter for surprise that the general imagination should have fastened on the atomic bomb, and even on the release of nuclear energy itself, as the source of a new species of danger for mankind, and that timorous philosophers should have been heard bemoaning one of the greatest of scientific achievements as a disaster to the world.

We shall not, I think, fall into this error. The atomic bomb may, indeed, represent a temporary climax in the enlistment of science for destruction. We shall look, as scientists, with even more interest and more eager hope than the rest of the world, to the efforts now being made to find, by agreement, an effective and lasting means of averting the danger threatened to civilization, from the misuse of what should be one of the greatest of the gifts of science to human welfare. It will be clear to us, however, that the atomic bomb presents a special case only of a much wider problem. This it has forced suddenly into the forefront of the world's attention; but the problem was there already, and would have presented itself for solution, even if the project for releasing nuclear energy had failed, or if it had never been undertaken. The recent hostilities saw only a beginning in the use of long-range projectiles, and the fact that the destructive possibilities of poisoning and infection were not actively exploited then must surely be attributed rather to lack of confidence in success than to any fidelity to conventions, or to compassionate reluctance. Nobody can guess what future discovery may offer, or predict what might be the result of committing effort and resources, on a scale comparable to those which produced the atomic bomb, to the general exploitation of other possibilities of using science as an agent of wholesale massacre and destruction. As scientists then, we must stand for the general principle and against all such perversion of the knowledge which we produce.

What, then, are we going to do about it? My own direct concern with science has been with its medical aspect, and I hope that nothing would tempt me to the pretence of offering a ready-made quack remedy for all the sickness of the world, or for that of science in its relation to such world problems. My first instinct is, rather, to invite you to consultation on a matter of diagnosis. And I assume that you will agree that we should restrict our consultation to the question which is our particular concern, and discuss whether anything is amiss with science, or with the aims and ideals with which we pursue it. Have we been astray, in regarding it as the first duty of science to seek the truth for its own sake, in holding the advancement of natural knowledge to be good in itself, independently of any value which its uses may have for the betterment of the conditions of man's life? Some would tell us to-day, indeed, that science has no right to such aloofness; that it is itself but a product and expression of the social progress of mankind, and can find its only proper aim and sanction in relation to social needs. They tell us even that this view was already held by such pioneers of our modern science as those who planned and brought about the foundation of the Royal Society, and that we have been at fault in departing from their precepts. Such a respect for ancient authority may seem strange from such a quarter; but, in any case, I find it difficult to convince myself that these early scientists were consistent followers of any such doctrine. It is true that Francis Bacon advocated researches "useful for man's life" as well as "for knowledge," but it was he also who wrote that "men are inclined to turn aside from their experiments for some practical application of them; like Atalanta they go aside to pick up the golden apple and let victory escape them; they shall seek for experiments of light, not for experiments of fruit." As for Robert Boyle, with his description of "our new philosophical college that values no knowledge but as it has a tendency to use," you would look in vain in his practice and that of his associates among the Royal Society's early Fellows, for any clear effect of such a principle. These men had, indeed, no pedantic aversion from practical problems, but, eager to explore all the joys of their new-found freedom to discover by experiment, they ventured with at least as much enthusiasm out into the unknown, without any thought of the application of what they might find.

When we come to the nineteenth century, with its great outburst of interest and activity in science and its applications, we find a striking unanimity among the leaders of that movement. One after another of these proclaims his conviction that the first duty of science is the discovery of truth, without reference to its uses. With equal conviction, however, they claim that the free pursuit of that unpractical ideal not only may, but commonly does, bring wider and more permanent benefit, even to the material aspects of human life and civilization, than are obtained by researches planned with a direct and limited object of useful discovery and invention. Most of us will to-day still agree with Professor Whitehead, that "in our most theoretical moods we may be nearest to our most practical inventions." Where industry, indeed, is under enlightened direction, this conviction has been notably effective in shaping even an industrial research policy, not on a basis of sentiment we may be sure, but of practical experience. Those, on the other hand, who are strongest in the faith that the proper objective of science is the service of social needs, accept researches of a nature most remote from any perceptible relation to practical use, as worthy to be promoted by an enlightened society or state, being also convinced that the most abstruse researches will eventually serve the happiness and prosperity of mankind. These varieties of personal conviction, then, seem to lead to practical policies of much the same kind; and, with regard to the particular matter of our discussion, there can be no suggestion that either conception of the true mission of science would give, or imply, a sanction for its misuse in the service of destruction. The independent pursuit of scientific knowledge does not imply indifference to the uses to which it is put when discovered; nor could a belief in social uses as its proper objective condone such perversion, unless it should be held to imply further that science must be the docile instrument of the political ideals and ambitions of rival states.

We cannot, it appears, arrive at our diagnosis of the malady on those lines and we must look elsewhere. After the news of the atomic bomb at Hiroshima, a letter which I wrote to a daily paper brought me comments from many people, and more than one of these raised the question whether the scientists of all countries could not bind themselves by something analogous to the Hippocratic Oath, which has exerted so powerful an influence on the ethical standards of medicine. In a recent address at Pittsburgh, at the centenary commemoration of the birth of George Westinghouse, my friend and colleague, A. V. Hill, developed the same idea in some detail; and I hope that those here who have not already done so will find opportunity to read Professor Hill's stirring presentation of that theme. Various associations and meetings of scientists in this country and in Britain, and of the representatives of many countries at a recent meeting in London of the Council of the International Scientific Unions, have formulated with varying degrees of elaboration, and recommended by impressive arrays of votes and signatures, their views and policies with regard to the position created, or forced into notice, by the use of nuclear energy as a weapon. As I have said already, we may find great encouragement in the substantial unanimity of attitude among scientists revealed by these various pronouncements, all being concerned to preserve the integrity of their life's work and to protect it from misuse. As I have suggested, however, the problem for science is a wider one than that with which some of these resolutions are concerned, and, like Professor Hill and others, I have been considering whether there might be some simpler and more inclusive profession of the scientific faith—of the principles of conduct by which we could agree to be guided, and which every scientist in the world, whatever his national loyalty or political creed, could properly be asked to accept. Let us see first whether our forerunners, of the days when nobody had thought of science as other than a completely international activity, made for themselves any rules which might help us.

We may safely regard the Second Charter of the Royal Society (1663) as representing views originating with its earliest Fellows, based on their still new experience, rather than with the Royal Patron who gave them the Charter. It directs the Fellows to apply their studies "to further promoting by the authority of experiments the sciences of natural things and of useful arts, to the glory of God the Creator and the advantage of the human race." And whatever conception each of us may form for himself of the eternal mysteries which are beyond the reach of our science, we need, even to-day, I suggest, no better definition than this of our proper objects and aspirations as scientists. The ideal which it presents should satisfy the advocates of the extension of scientific knowledge as an aim in itself, as well as those who insist on its service of social needs, but it does not lead us directly to a simple and specific diagnosis of a cause for the malady, by which this ideal is now threatened with corrosion and defacement.

More than sixty years later Benjamin Franklin gave a simpler and more practical definition, framed with that terse economy of words which marks the style of those who know the use of our English language at its noble best. It was in the form of a question, requiring an affirmative answer from every candidate for admission to the Junto, that earliest of American learned associations, to which "The American Philosophical Society held at Philadelphia for promoting useful knowledge" traces its origin. "Do you love truth for truth's sake, and will you endeavour impartially to find and receive it for yourself, and communicate it to others?" If we were asked to propound an oath, a formal profession of faith and conduct, for the acceptance of every scientist in the world to-day, I should doubt our ability to improve on this one of more than two centuries ago. If we give to each word of this declaration, as we should, the full weight of its proper meaning, it embodies an uncompromising rule of scientific conduct and, therewith, a charter of scientific freedom. "To communicate impartially to others the scientific truth, which one has found and received impartially for himself"—here, surely, is a rule which, if the scientists of the world could have accepted it and kept it faithfully, would have made it impossible for the world to misuse science as in these recent years. Secrecy, as Franklin saw, is alien to the very spirit of science, and it is the main infection, I suggest to you, from which science sickens to-day.

If you glance back over the history of modern science, from its beginning in the sixteenth and seventeenth centuries, I think that you will find that it has always been so. Secrecy, due in this case to a morbid sensitiveness to criticism or controversy, blemished even the noble character of Isaac Newton, and cast a cloud on the splendour of his fame. It almost robbed the world of the *Principia*, that crowning achievement of the human mind, and it involved Newton in an exchange of claims and accusations with Leibnitz, discreditable to both of them as well as to the societies which espoused their causes, and even threatening a rift, on national lines, in the completely international community of science in the Europe of those days. We have all been long familiar, from direct experience, with the breaks which secrecy may cause in the clear and confident understanding between individual colleagues in science, and with the embarrassment which it may introduce into what should be most helpful relations, between workers in free and academic institutions and their colleagues who are engaged in special researches for industry or government; but these, till recently, have been but small clouds in a generally clear sky. The right and the duty to tell the world the truth which we discover, without regard to the interests of any person, prejudice, creed, political theory, or national policy, has been the central item in the charter of our scientific freedom.

The effect of war on this freedom of science became prominent first with the earlier world war. Scientists, loyally ready then as more recently to aid their nation's cause, thought it little sacrifice to submit to an unfamiliar and unwelcome secrecy, when others were sacrificing all their natural instincts and often their lives. And in 1918 most of the scientists, like most of the warriors, returned joyfully to normal life and normal standards, with the hope that such a call would never come again. When this hope proved vain, the call was for science and scientists as never before to meet the new threat from an enemy who had already enlisted most of the science of his great nation in secret preparation for an attack on the world's freedom. And to meet this menace we free peoples found ourselves obliged to submit again to the invasion of our scientific activities by secrecy, to a degree beyond any which had so far been regarded as possible. Secrecy percolated into domains which all earlier wars had held sacred; so that we, for example, whose work was in the medical sciences found ourselves involved in an inconsistency which still paid a conventional respect to that immunity of medical equipment and personnel which a more scrupulous age had established, but compelled us, in the name of total war, to throw a veil of secrecy over the new discoveries which could make their work of mercy really effective. To all this and much more we loyally submitted. And now that science has done its part, and the war has been won, we look for the freedom that victory was to ensure. Do we find it? Or do we find science still wearing its wartime fetters, in the interests of a right assumed for any nation, at peace, to make secret preparation for the destruction of its neighbours?

What, then, are we to do, as the scientists, not of one nation or group of nations, but of all or, if not yet all, of as many as we can effectively reach with a call for such common action? Let it be understood, first, that there can be no question of anything less than perfect fidelity to pledges given and not yet relinquished, or of any claim by scientists to more than their due and democratic share in shaping the policies of the nations which claim their loyalties. That being understood, we have surely the right and the duty to give urgent warning of any danger threatened by those policies to the integrity of science, which we, the world's scientists, should hold as a sacred trust, not for any nation, but for the world. I hold it to be our right and our duty to unite in telling the world insistently, that if national policies fail to free science in peace from the secrecy which it accepted as a necessity of war, they will poison its very spirit; that those men whom the world can least afford to spare from the service of science, the men with the vision and the inspiration that can survive only in freedom, will be diverted from the lines of research in which their genius would most naturally find its fruition, or will even decide to give their service to humanity in other spheres than that of science; that science will languish, and that all the fair promise which it offers of a harvest of human prosperity, culture, and happiness will be blighted and withered. We need only look at Hitler's Germany to see how the enslavement of science, to prepare in secret for war, can in a few years destroy much of the true scientific activity which, not long ago, stood high among the gifts of a great nation to the world. On such a matter we must be clear and uncompromising in our attitude. We may be told that the abandonment of national secrecy in science would make the retention of any kind of military secrecy impossible, and that this would compromise rights of national sovereignty. We must reply, I think, that as scientists we are concerned, not with the maintenance of military secrecy or of national sovereignty, but with that of scientific freedom; that if national sovereignty means a right of any nation to prepare in secret for the destruction of others, and to use science for that purpose, its maintenance will destroy the spirit of science as we have known it, while it brings all civilization within sight of its end; and that only an abandonment of that claim will make it possible for us to rebuild an international community in science, and therewith to remove from the world the threat of a measureless disaster.

Apart from such united protest, can we do anything more practical and immediate? We should, of course, use all our effort and influence to increase the effectiveness and the range of the international scientific unions which came into existence after the First World War, have survived the Second, and are now to be one of the activities recognized and supported by UNESCO. The discussions in which we have been engaged in these days of international conference, with the promise they afford of a persistent, coördinated effort to promote meetings of the international unions and of wider international congresses, are all of great value. Even more important, however, is a constant effort to secure the removal of any barriers which still prevent us from wandering freely and informally into the institutes and laboratories of our fellow scientists in other lands, as many of us can remember doing in earlier days. But, above all, we ought to keep clearly before us the fact that the future of science is in the hands of the young men entering its service. I think that we might consider whether the universities of all the nations where freedom is valued could be moved to common action to ensure that these new recruits to science learn the full meaning of its freedom, and the world's need that they should be alert to defend its integrity. Would it be possible, I wonder, for the world's universities to require an undertaking from every candidate for graduation in science, or, for that matter, in any other department of true knowledge, such as Franklin prescribed for admission to his Junto—to love truth for truth's sake, and impartially to find, receive, and communicate it? Or, since the most potent teacher is example, could not the universities of the world unite in banning secrecy from any activities of their departments? In many countries, if not in all, the times are past when science in the universities can look for adequate means to charitable endowments. Academic science everywhere must increasingly look to the state or to industry for financial support. Is it possible to consider an agreement by which the universities, of separate nations first, perhaps, and eventually of all, would bind themselves never to accept contracts for research, either from state or industry, except under conditions ensuring complete freedom to make known the results to all the world? It may be that in some country the universities have already made such an agreement effective; but, in any case, its general acceptance would surely do something to establish a tradition of full freedom for science, with those to whom the torch will soon be handed.

Let me, in conclusion, say but a few words on the place of science in the moral structure of our civilization. As the Middle Ages ended, there grew, with the revival of ancient learning and the spirit of mental enterprise which it liberated, a new body of secular knowledge, won by man's own effort and inquiry and, therefore, distinguished as human or humane, from the knowledge termed divine, as having been revealed by God and interpreted by the Church. It might similarly have been distinguished as profane knowledge, from that which was sacred. I think that there can be no doubt that all the natural and mathematical science which then existed would have been included in this new tradition of humanism. Nomenclature suffers curious and anomalous changes of use; and we, who have allowed the word science, meaning all knowledge, often to become limited in common usage to that aspect of knowledge which is the subject of our own studies and practice, are not in a strong position to criticize our colleagues whose work is in literature and the fine arts, in history, moral philosophy, and theology, when they claim for these alone the description "humane studies," or speak of them more briefly as "the humanities." But, while we may condone this as a freak of terminology, we must strongly resist any attempt to base on it, and on the verbal ambiguity in which modern usage has involved it, an implication that only these studies can create and strengthen an attitude to the world and its affairs which is humane in the moral sense, and that science, by contrast, creates an outlook which sees only material issues and is blind to moral ones. The new revelation of danger to the world, from the use of science in war, has given an obvious opportunity to those who sincerely dislike science, and have viewed its growing influence with distrust and resentment. It is not surprising, then, to encounter the warning that science is leading the world headlong to disaster, and that only the humanities can bring back to it the moral strength and the wisdom needed to give it peace and safety; but I say that we ought most firmly to contest any such implication. We ourselves deplore and denounce the misuse of science as a weapon, and desire with a painful urgency to see it ended; but to be made an instrument of war is not to be the cause of the moral and mental attitude by which wars are engendered. Theological controversy, differences of dogma and of ritual, have, in the past, formed a basis of provocation for wars which have laid large parts of Europe waste. They are still a cause of political antagonism and fratricidal violence in Europe and farther east. Historical truth has been and is still being debased and perverted to arouse national ambitions, rivalries and antagonisms, which political philosophy, literary and pictorial art, poetry and rhetoric can be misused to fan into open flame. We shall not, on that account, accuse theology, history, literature, or the fine arts of being, in themselves, the causes of wars; but we shall not accept the imputation for science, or concede to studies which have, at best, not prevented wars hitherto, the possession of an exclusive secret for educating the moral sense of mankind into abandoning them now. The moral education of mankind needs all that can be offered by man's sincere seeking for the truth in any of its aspects, and by any means. Science has been associated with the other cultural activities of mankind in UNESCO, the Educational, Scientific and Cultural Organization of the United Nations; and science has indeed a contribution of its own to make to the cultural and moral equipment which mankind so urgently needs, not less than that made by any body of knowledge, art, or educational discipline. It is not without significance that, whereas history, literature, art, and even religion, all have national characters and local attachments, science alone of man's major intellectual interests has no frontiers and no national varieties; that science, like peace, is one and indivisible. We should admit no claim of the studies which concern themselves with the past achievements of mankind, however great and noble, to an exclusive value as a moral discipline, or to superiority, as a training for men to face the problems of the modern world, over science which looks to the future and strives forward and upward towards higher points of view, commanding an ever receding horizon of knowledge of material nature, and binding an ever widening range of natural forces to the service of mankind and the enlargement of human happiness. And science, we should insist, better than any other discipline, can hold up to its students and followers an ideal of patient devotion to the search for objective truth, with vision unclouded by personal or political motive, not tolerating any lapse from precision or neglect of any anomaly, fearing only prejudice and preconception, accepting nature's answers humbly and with courage, and giving them to the world with an un-flinching fidelity. The world cannot afford to lose such a contri-bution to the moral framework of its civilization, and science can continue to offer it only if science can remain free.

EXPERIMENT IN MEDICINE*

I HAVE been asked to speak about the history of the experimental method in medicine, with particular reference to the nineteenth century. This indication, though I do not propose to regard it as setting a limit, seems to have a special fitness, since it is to the nineteenth century, and especially to its latter half, that we must look for the effective beginning and astonishingly rapid development, the veritable outburst, indeed, of activity in the application of the experimental method to medicine, which opened the new era of medical progress in which we are living to-day. It is curious, perhaps, that this should have come so late in the history of science. For medicine had figured early in man's attempts to understand nature and his relation to it, and many departments of science which have long ago achieved recognition as independent bodies of knowledge originated as aspects of the physician's equipment—botany, for example, zoology and chemistry, as well as human anatomy and physiology, which still retain their attachment to the medical group of the scientific disciplines. From this point of view, then, it is not surprising to find two physicians, William Gilbert and William Harvey, as the leaders in this country of the scientific revolution which had begun in Europe in 1543 with the publication, within a few weeks of one another, of two books—one by Copernicus of Cracow, *De Revolutionibus Orbium Coelestium*, and the other by Vesalius of Padua, *De Humani Corporis Fabrica*. Both Gilbert and Harvey, we may be proud to remember, studied and first graduated in medicine here, in Cambridge. Gilbert (1544-1605), born 1544, only a year after Copernicus and Vesalius had published, was the leading English physician of his day, and physician to Queen Elizabeth, but was rightly more famous as the first experimental investigator of the properties of magnetic materials and of the nature of magnetism and electricity. He was actually the first to coin the word "electric," from the Greek *electron*, amber, describing as the *vis electrica* the property of attracting

---

* A lecture delivered in the Mill Lane Lecture Room, Cambridge, on 2nd March, 1946, in a course arranged by the History of Science Committee.

other bodies which certain substances, amber among them, acquire on being rubbed—a fact said to have been known to Thales of Miletus as early as 600 B.C.

William Harvey belonged to the next generation, having been born in 1578, thirty-four years later than Gilbert. He was physician to Charles the First and to Francis Bacon, and his work as an experimenter was directly relevant to our subject of to-day; for Harvey, who published in 1628 his *De Motu Cordis*, giving not only the first description of the double circulation of the blood through the lungs and the body at large, but convincing proof of it by experiments on animals of different kinds and on man himself, became thus not only the first, but probably the greatest hitherto, of all experimental workers in the medical field of the sciences.

It may seem to you that, by starting thus with events earlier by two or three centuries than those of my particular subject I run the risk of approaching it asymptotically, without reaching it, at least, in the normal span of a lecture. Any consideration, however, of the significance of that outburst of experimental activity in medical science in the middle of the nineteenth century, in the continuation and extension of which we are now living, raises the questions, why it began about a century ago, why it was so long delayed, what had gone before it, and at what interval. When we find the association of the experimental method with medicine already so close at the turn of the sixteenth century, and its direct application to the advancement of medical science already made to such triumphant purpose by William Harvey, we are bound to inquire why its use by those concerned with medicine fell so largely into abeyance during more than two centuries, and why it then reappeared, remained and continued, as the basis of the imposing advance, on an ever-widening front, which we are now witnessing. For we must remember that Harvey was not an accidental or unconscious innovator, but one fully aware of the revolutionary significance of the method of direct, experimental inquiry which he was using, and which, not many years earlier, he could only have used at peril of his life for heresy. He was a very embodiment of the great adventurous spirit of that age, as it shook itself free from the bonds of orthodoxy and ancient tradition in science, and advanced boldly into the unknown in the new light of direct observation and experiment. "Not from books but from dissections," writes Harvey in his own most famous book; and in the introduction to his other, less known but much larger work, full of original observation on the generation and reproduction of animals, he recurs again and again to this theme. "It were disgraceful, therefore," he exclaims, "did we take the reports of others upon trust, and go on coining crude problems out of these, and on them hanging knotty and captious and petty disputations. Nature herself is to be addressed; the paths she shows us are to be boldly trodden; for thus, and whilst we consult our proper senses . . . shall we penetrate at length into the heart of her mystery." And, finally, he bequeathes to the Royal College of Physicians a fund for an annual Oration, in which the Fellows shall be enjoined "to seek and to study out the secrets of nature by means of experiment."

Why then, with this resplendent example before them, did the physicians show so little apparent inclination to obey this annual injunction, for most of two centuries after it was first given? A full explanation would involve a complexity of factors, but I think that we may identify a principal one in the fact that further progress in knowledge of the functions of the living organism, in health and disease, beyond the point reached by Harvey in his first bold experimental adventure, would of necessity be slow and capricious, so long as the only instrumental methods available for experiments, and the data of fundamental science required for their devising, were as crude and as fragmentary as those available to Harvey himself. We must remember that Harvey was not only a pioneer in the use of experiment in medical science, but was also, like Gilbert before him, one of the pioneers, in this country and in the world, of the use of the method of direct observation and experiment, and of the unfettered interpretation of the results of these, over the whole range of science.

To those, therefore, who came immediately after Harvey—that wonderful group of early Fellows of the Royal Society, including Boyle, Hooke, Wren, Mayow and Lower, of whom only Mayow and Lower had medical training, and only the latter was a Fellow of the Physicians' College—the natural aim was not merely an extension of Harvey's observations, such as Lower, in particular, was able to make at certain points, but a much wider quest for the fundamental laws and data of physics and chemistry, without which little further progress was to be expected on Harvey's lines. How far the men of this group advanced is sufficiently indicated by the fact that they already came to recognize the fundamental identity of the processes of combustion and of respiration. They recognized the need of the body, in order to maintain its vital activity and production of heat, for the same constituent of the air as was required for and used in the support of combustion—a constituent which they called, indeed, the "nitroäerial spirit," but which was, beyond doubt, the same as that which was to be rediscovered and isolated, a century later, by Priestley and by Lavoisier, and to be given by the latter its final name, Oxygen. This lapse of a century, before progress was resumed from the point to which Boyle, Hooke, Mayow and their colleagues had brought it, was in large measure due to the plausible but fallacious phlogiston hypothesis of Stahl, a German physician and vitalist philosopher. This seized the minds of his generation with the force of a dogma, so that its framework governed and distorted the interpretation of all chemical observations during this long interval; even Priestley still described oxygen, when he first separated it in pure form, as "dephlogisticated air." It would not be reasonable, however, to suggest that, without this diversion, the discoveries of Boyle, Hooke, Mayow and their associates would have sufficed, by themselves, to produce such a revival of physiological progress as came later, after those of Lavoisier. The phlogistic theory was just one of the factors in the delay which followed Harvey's flying start; and Lavoisier's final disposal of it, and his establishment of oxidation as a central feature of the life process, were only among the conditions required for a steady, unbroken progress of medical knowledge by experiment.

The period between Harvey and the mid-nineteenth century was not, of course, barren of all progress in the medical sciences. The general aim and continuous tendency in that interval, however, were towards laying the ground-work of accurate observation, classification and description. Meanwhile, of the experimental structure which was ultimately to be reared upon this descriptive basis, only certain detached items arose, at irregular intervals, at the hands of individual workers of genius. This classificatory and descriptive tendency was characteristic of activity in the whole of the biological group of the sciences during this period of about two centuries; and it is very far from my intention to depreciate the order of knowledge which it produced, and still produces, or to suggest for it a rank below that of the knowledge which can only be won by experimental intervention. As a detailed and accurate survey and charting of the territory to be explored it was, at the very least, a necessary prelude to the full-scale experimental invasion. Of the physicians, then, who followed Harvey in this period, from Sydenham (1624–89), Harvey's partial contemporary, on to the great medical figures of the earlier half of the nineteenth century, such as the famous Guy's Hospital trio, Bright (1789–1858), Addison (1798–1860) and Hodgkin (1798–1866), all were observers and faithful recorders, classifiers who accurately differentiated and described diseases and labelled them for identification, as field naturalists describe and name new animals or plants, rather than experimental investigators of causes. An extreme example, a caricature, as it were, of this tendency, is offered by Boissier de Sauvages, the French physician who, in 1768, published a system in which he classified the known diseases into 10 classes, 295 genera, and 2400 species. For the experimental investigation of causes, the scientific tools and the fundamental data were still not available. Of those rare enthusiasts who kept the experimental tradition in medicine alive during this interval not all, by any means, were physicians. Stephen Hales (1677–1761), a man with some of the authentic touch of Harvey, who discovered and measured the root-pressure of the sap in plants and the blood-pressure in a mammalian artery, and who first described the reflex actions mediated by the spinal cord of a frog deprived of its brain, was a clergyman —the perpetual curate of Teddington. John Hunter (1728–93), whose achievements first detached surgery as a profession from the barber's craft, and who was one of the greatest of workers in the descriptive fields of human and comparative anatomy and pathology, also used the experimental method in his studies on growth, and knew well its worth—witness his famous recommendation to his pupil, Edward Jenner, ". . . but why think? Why not try the experiment?" Priestley and

Lavoisier, collateral discoverers of oxygen, were also physiological experimenters on its significance for the life process.
Edward Jenner, faithful to Hunter's precept, subjected to the
test of deliberate experiment the reputed immunity from smallpox of milkers whose hands had been infected with cowpox.
His little book describing his discovery of vaccination, published
just before the end of the eighteenth century, may be regarded,
perhaps, as the earliest true forerunner of the modern, experimental period. For Jenner, as we now know, was dealing with
infection by one of the sub-microscopic agents to which it
has become customary in recent years to limit the originally
inclusive term "virus." He was observing, long in advance
of his age, the modification of the virus of human smallpox
by transfer to a less susceptible subject species, the cow; and
he proved, in effect, that the virus, so mitigated in virulence
that it would now cause only a relatively trivial and localized
infection when inoculated into man, would still confer thereby
a substantial immunity to the original, unmitigated virus of
smallpox. So described, Jenner's method seems like a very
modern immunological procedure, though he himself was
far, of course, from the knowledge which now makes possible
such a description of his findings. The fact that he proceeded
from mere observation to experiment gave to his work an
authority and a convincing quality, and a new order of practical
success. His contemporaries in this and other countries rightly
acclaimed Jenner's achievement in offering protection to mankind
from one of its most dreaded afflictions; we to-day can look
back to him as a pioneer of the experimental method, venturing
forward, long before the light of knowledge shone brightly
enough to make possible an ordered progress, along the path
into which he had boldly groped his way.

In this period, before experiment became recognized as the
regular method of ensuring progress in medical knowledge,
other examples could be found of observations, correct in
themselves, which failed to carry conviction because, unlike
Jenner's, they lacked the reinforcement of experimental proof.
Long before there was any talk of vitamins it had been observed
that scurvy could be cured by giving fresh fruit and vegetables.
The crude discovery appears, indeed, to have been made, forgotten and remade in each century from the sixteenth to the

7

eighteenth; in the eighteenth century Dr. James Lind and Captain James Cook both clearly recorded the observation. In 1840 Steinhäuser described the cure of rickets by cod-liver oil. Yet the significance of these observations remained obscure, and they fell largely into oblivion. As the late Mr. Wilfrid Trotter pointed out, in a lecture on "General Ideas in Medicine": "The truth remained undistinguished, among innumerable opinions current about these diseases, for 150 years in one case and 80 years in the other." It could not, in fact, be made effective until, in the present century, the chemical and other items of scientific equipment became available, which enabled these problems to be approached by the experimental method; but then with the result that the vitamin C and vitamin D were obtained, their structures were identified and they were made artifically in the laboratory. A distinguished Chinese colleague informs me that the ancient medical writings of his country contain clear evidence that thyroid gland was used there for treating myxoedema over a thousand years ago. It is certain, however, that this empirical discovery, if it was really made, had been as completely lost to memory in China as elsewhere, till the treatment was rediscovered in 1891 by a rational application of experimentally won knowledge.

Other examples could be given; but I think that the general outline of the answer to our problem already emerges. Although the application of the experimental method to medicine was given such an early start by the work of one of our greatest of scientific pioneers, it had to wait for the further gradual building of a firmer basis of observation and record, for the anatomy of the body to be described in detail and some of its diseases identified, and for the preparatory advances to be achieved in other and more fundamental departments of science, before its renewed and permanent progress, on an extended and ever-widening front, could begin. Experimental medicine, in fact, could move forward only as one aspect of a general advance of the experimental sciences, and following some of these at the varying interval which was needed for the learning and development by medicine, for its own purposes, of knowledge and methods which other departments of experimental science had acquired for theirs.

Where then are we to place the true beginning of the experimental era in medical science? The discovery in the 1830's,
by Sir Charles Bell in London and by Magendie in Paris, of
the separate sensory and motor functions of the dorsal and ventral
roots by which the peripheral nerves are connected to the
spinal cord, takes high rank as an experimental achievement;
but it was still too isolated, I think, to be reckoned as even the
earliest item of the great revival and development. It came at a
time when the great acceleration in the advance of the primary
sciences was only just beginning. Wöhler had made urea by
artificial synthesis in 1828, proving that organic substances were
just chemical compounds of a special natural origin, and did not
require any mysterious vital activity for their production;
and the progress of organic chemistry, from then onwards, has
been an essential condition and concomitant of the progress of
experimental science in the medical field. In 1831 Faraday discovered electro-magnetic induction, and opened the great era
of electrical invention and practical application; and this, too,
was to become a very important factor in the progress of experimental physiology and medicine. Another was the rapid progress in the mechanical and optical perfection of the compound
microscope. Leeuwenhoek, indeed, the linen-draper and optician
of Delft, had marvellously seen and recognizably figured yeast
cells and bacteria with his simple lenses as early as the 1680's;
but there can be no doubt that the emergence of the sciences of
bacteriology and general microbiology, with their tremendous
influence on the experimental advances of the knowledge of the
causes, and therewith of the treatment, of infectious diseases,
could not have occurred during the latter half of the nineteenth
century without the efficient microscopes which were then
becoming available. Yet another condition for really rapid
advance, on one side of experimental medicine, was the discovery
and practical introduction of methods of chemical anaesthesia.
We may note that the essential discovery came, here again, from
investigators outside the medical field. Humphry Davy discovered the anaesthetic action of nitrous oxide in 1800. The
similar action of ether was observed in 1818 by Faraday, then
Davy's assistant at the Royal Institution, and shortly afterwards
by several workers in the U.S.A. Then, after a somewhat
chequered and controversial history in the initial stages, the

method was practically applied in major surgery, in the U.S.A. and in this country, in 1846. In the following year came Simpson's use of chloroform in midwifery. So, again by the middle of the century, the way was open for anaesthetics to widen greatly the range and the freedom of the experimental method in physiology, pathology and the related departments of medical science.

I think that we may date the beginning in the nineteenth century of the great period of activity in experimental medicine from the work of two great French investigators, Claude Bernard (1813–78) and Louis Pasteur (1822–95). With Bernard, pupil of Magendie and his successor in 1855, modern physiology and functional biochemistry may be said to have begun. He showed the function of the pancreatic juice as the major digestive agent of all three main classes of food substances; he discovered the carbohydrate store of glycogen in the liver and the muscles; he introduced the conception of internal secretion into the blood in describing the liver's functions; and he first observed the vaso-motor action of sympathetic nerves. While from his own experiments Bernard thus obtained and planted seedlings of knowledge from which has grown so much of modern physiology, he was, in a wider sense, a biological philosopher of the highest rank, perceiving, as Dr. Singer writes, that the characteristic of living things is the preservation of internal conditions. In Bernard's own rather paradoxical phrase, "vital mechanisms have only one *object*, that of preserving constant the conditions of life in the internal environment"—a conception which is still dominant in a wide range of physiology. Bernard wrote also an *Introduction to the Study of Experimental Medicine*, still abundantly worth reading as a manual of wise doctrine, on methods of research and inter-pretation in medicine and biology; it is obtainable in a good translation, with a characteristic introduction by the late Lawrence Henderson of Harvard, who inherited and transmitted more, perhaps, of Bernard's widely philosophical outlook than most modern workers in physiology and biochemistry. Only a little later than Bernard, and next to him in influence on the growth of modern experimental physiology, was Carl Ludwig (1816–95), who, after holding Chairs at Zürich and Vienna, began his historic tenure of the Chair of Physiology at Leipzig in 1865.

Several of those who were founders of our own British Schools of Experimental Physiology studied with Bernard or with

Ludwig, who thus came to exercise a potent influence on the development of experimental medicine in this country. Michael Foster and John Burdon Sanderson were both pupils of Bernard at different dates, as both were later assistant professors under William Sharpey, the Professor of Anatomy and Physiology at University College, London, whom Burdon-Sanderson later succeeded there. In 1870 Foster moved to Cambridge, being appointed, on Thomas Huxley's recommendation, Praelector of Physiology in Trinity College—an appointment of great moment to this University, for from it grew not only the department of physiology, but all the departments here in which biology is treated as a subject of research by experiment. Foster was greater as a teacher of the methods and as a critic of the results of research, than as an investigator with his own hands. Through the brilliant group of his early pupils, Gaskell, who worked also with Ludwig before he returned to settle in Cambridge, Langley, Newall Martin, first Professor of Physiology at Johns Hopkins University, Baltimore, F. M. Balfour (Embryology), Roy (Experimental Pathology), and others, Foster's influence on the revival and initiation of the experimental method, not only in physiology but in a wide range of the medical sciences, spread not only in this country, but far beyond it. His pupils and their pupils played an important role in putting British physiology high in the world's esteem. To mention them and their work individually would take us much too far. Let it suffice to-day to mention the work of Charles Sherrington, with its profound influence not only on the physiology of the nervous system, but on clinical neurology as an experimental science; and to mention also, as almost the last act of Michael Foster as Professor here, the introduction to the Cambridge school of Frederick Gowland Hopkins, and all that that has meant in enabling biochemistry to make its great and growing contribution to medicine as an experimental science. At Oxford Burdon-Sanderson was appointed Professor of Physiology in 1882, and introduced there, twelve years later than Foster in Cambridge, the application of the experimental method to physiology, spreading, in due course, to the other medical sciences. Burdon-Sanderson, in his own researches, was a pioneer in this country of the application of electrical methods to the recording of physiological events, by use of what seem now the rather crude appliances of those days, in the light of the astonishing developments of refined electrical equipment in recent years. One other investigator and teacher may be mentioned who left his mark on the development of British physiology—Edward Albert Schäfer, who like Foster and Burdon-Sanderson had been a pupil of William Sharpey, and later took the name Sharpey-Schafer in honour of his great teacher's memory. He will be specially remembered for his influence on Britain's contribution to the physiology of the ductless glands—endocrinology, one of the developments of physiology which, in due course, has most directly influenced clinical medicine and therapeutics.

Louis Pasteur, in whose researches we can find the real beginning of medical knowledge of infectious diseases as due to the invasion of the body and its tissues by micro-organisms and viruses, was not a medical man, not even a biologist, in his training and his earliest researches. He was a chemist, a mineralogist and a crystallographer. It was Pasteur who discovered the mirror-image asymmetry of the crystals of the two types of tartaric acid, the connexion of this with the opposite actions of the two types on the plane of polarized light, and the relation of both types to the optically inactive racemic acid. His interest was attracted by the selective digestion of one of these isomers by a mould—a *Penicillium* in fact—and then, with a mind rendered alert to the idea of fermentation as due to living micro-organisms, he received an additional opportunity for such studies through his appointment to a Chair at Lille, a centre of the brewing and distilling industries. Thus, from tackling problems of the making of vinegar and of sound beer, and of the wine diseases of his native district in France, and from recognizing the micro-organisms variously involved, Pasteur arrived at the conception of all kinds of fermentation and putrefaction as due to the growth of living yeasts and bacteria, not generated spontaneously, but started, in each case, by the introduction, deliberate or accidental, of the living organism concerned or its resting spores. In obtaining this definitely negative answer to the question of spontaneous generation, a matter of renewed controversy over several centuries, Pasteur's work was reinforced and its conclusions established by the researches at the Royal Instutution of another great non-medical scientist, John Tyndall. Then Pasteur, having cured diseases in wine, was called upon to deal with those of silkworms, and then to pass from "pebrine" in silkworms to anthrax in cattle. Meanwhile Lister, in Britain, had applied Pasteur's discoveries to elucidate the nature and the means of prevention of septic infections, and had thereby produced a revolution in surgery even greater, I think, than that which had resulted from the introduction of anaesthesia. Robert Koch, in Germany, had produced the first clear and complete experimental identification of a specific micro-organism, the bacillus of anthrax, as the cause of a particular disease, and had introduced methods which immensely facilitated the separation of organisms in pure culture. And from these beginnings, at the hands of pupils and followers of these men too numerous for mention, came the great revolution, due to microbiology, in the experimental pathology and ultimately in the treatment of infections—one of the great glories of experimental science in the latter half of the nineteenth, and in what we have yet seen of the present century. Starting with infections due to the microscopic plants, the bacteria, it had to include later those due to microscopic animals, the protozoa, to the spirochaetes, concerning which opinion has varied as to their proper classification, and, most recently, to the viruses, on one of which, as we have seen, Jenner had unconsciously conducted, nearly a century in advance of its time, a pioneer research in immunology. The experimental demonstration of the existence of viruses, infective agents with units too small to be stopped by a bacteria-proof filter, or to be seen with the highest powers of an ordinary microscope, came with the closing years of the nineteenth and the earliest years of the twentieth century.

Another event should be briefly mentioned, which also occurred in the nineteenth century's last decade—the discovery by Röntgen of the X-rays. This opened a new era in physical research which, at second hand, has profoundly affected the methods available to medical research, as well as to practical diagnosis and treatment; and the most recent dramatic advances in nuclear physics promise likewise, for medical science and practice, a whole new outfit of powerful equipment.

I have tried to show something of the origins, in the latter half of the nineteenth century, of the great experimental era in medical science and its applications in practice, in the midst of which we are still living. To attempt to trace, in any detail, the developments from any one of these sources, even in one country, not to mention those in the world at large, would lead me far beyond the scope and intention of this lecture. One characteristic feature of developments in more recent years has been the use of the methods and principles learned in the laboratory, and of others developed specially for the particular purpose, in researches made directly on the functions of the normal man and on the disturbances produced in these by disease. This is a kind of investigation which, one must feel, would have been particularly congenial to the spirit of William Harvey himself, if he could walk the earth again to-day and avail himself of the methods which modern science affords. Only last year, we, his friends and colleagues, and the world at large, lost, by the death of Sir Thomas Lewis, a most determined British advocate and a brilliant practitioner of the advancement of medical knowledge by such direct experimental methods in the clinic.

There are many departments of medical knowledge and practice from which it would be possible to illustrate the advances which have resulted, in this twentieth century, from the great experimental movement which began in that which preceded it, by comparing the position of knowledge and its applications at the opening of the present century, when some of us were students in hospital, to that at the present day.

Let me conclude my survey by sketching such a comparison very briefly, in the case of one aspect only of medicine—one which, I think, would be accorded high rank in interest by mankind at large—that of the medicinal treatment of disease. The effect produced on this by the experimental advance must naturally lag behind the changes in some other branches of medical knowledge. It would clearly be necessary to know something definite about the cause of a disease before the problem could be taken in hand of discovering, by experiment, a method of treatment, whether for preventing or curing it, on a rational, scientific basis. It is hardly too much to say that, at the beginning of the present century, there were only the first tentative beginnings of a therapeutics with a scientific basis of any kind. In the cases of some two or three of the long list of old-established remedies—the use of cinchona and its alkaloids for malarial fevers, for example, or of ipecacuanha for tropical dysentery—the progress of experimental medicine, as it revealed the infective causes, was just beginning to find a rational basis for applications which, through centuries past, had been based on crude impression and tradition. For a few others, there was unusual scientific warrant in genuinely experimental investigations made long before the experimental era, such as Withering's classical investigation of the use of the foxglove as a remedy in heart-disease, dating from 1785. A very few remedies directly derived from the teachings of experimental research had, indeed, come recently into use, still as rather exciting novelties, when this century began. Such were the treatment of myxoedema with thyroid gland substance and of diphtheria with the specific antitoxin. Such few, however, stood out in vivid contrast to the great majority of the drugs and medicaments then being given with very little scientific basis and, in any case, with no hope or intention beyond that of making the patient comfortable, mitigating the symptoms of his disease, and thus giving nature the best chance of dealing with its cause. There was great talk still in those days of the "vis medicatrix naturae." One of my clearest memories of my clinical teachers, at the opening of this century, is of the contemptuous scepticism with which the more scientifically candid of them regarded all but a few of the medicines which tradition and the expectation of their patients nevertheless made it almost inevitable that they should continue to prescribe. "I have seen it do good, and, in any case, it won't do harm," was high praise for a remedy in those days. And I do not think that the experimental method has had a more revolutionary effect at any time, on any department of medical science or practice, than that which it has produced during the present century in therapeutics. The physician finds himself now equipped with a whole range of remedial or preventive agents dealing directly with the causes of diseases and aimed at the elimination of these, and not merely at the alleviation of their effects.

Let us very briefly consider the effect of this change on the treatment of two of the major groups of diseases, of which the causes have been revealed by experimental researches in physiology, biochemistry, and infective pathology. We have, on the one hand, diseases of deficiency, due to the absence, or the defect, of principles essential to healthy growth and function, which may be hormones, formed by the body's own glands of internal secretion, or vitamins, present in a complete and unsophisticated diet. In discovering the causes of these, experimental science has directly revealed the specific remedies—the missing principles themselves, of course, when supplied in the appropriate amounts; and, for a whole range of both hormones and vitamins, which, but a few decades ago, had seemed most probably to be for ever intangible by experiment, research in endocrinology and biochemistry has identified the missing principles, and organic chemistry has found ways of making them artificially, till the resources of the Greek lexicon and of a single alphabet are becoming strained by the problem of their nomenclature. By way of examples, contrast the helpless attitude of medicinal treatment to diabetes, pernicious anaemia, and rickets when this century began, with its confidence of effective intervention now.

On the other hand we have the diseases of infection, due to the presence and multiplication in the body of invading organisms, foreign to its nature and inimical to its functions. From the seed planted by Jenner, when it had been stimulated and nourished by the new knowledge which came with Pasteur, Koch, and their followers, there germinated presently the new science of immunology, dealing with nature's own method of combating an infection and establishing a specific resistance to it, lasting sometimes for a lifetime. This was found to be due to the acquisition by the victim's own body, of a new habit of forming specific antidotes to the invader or its poison. Then came practical applications of this new knowledge by the use of natural remedies, imitating or supplementing this natural reaction to immunity. Beginning towards the end of the nineteenth century with the antitoxic sera, prepared against the poisons of the bacilli of tetanus and diphtheria by Behring and Kitasato in Germany and by Roux and Yersin in France, this new method of dealing with the causes of infection, by specifically reinforcing the natural mechanisms of resistance, produced a whole range of sera for curative, and of vaccines and toxoids for preventive treatment, the latter being used to excite the natural reaction of immunity in the subject's own body, in advance of his exposure to infection. Contrast, again, by way of examples, the almost helpless attitude of medicine to diphtheria in the closing decades of the last century with the position now, when this menace of child life has been banished by specific inoculation from a number of large cities on the North American continent, and when we are entitled to demand its banishment from our own; or contrast the terrible problems of suffering, as well as of military efficiency, presented by tetanus in the Franco-Prussian war and by enteric fever in the South African war, with experience in the war just ended, in which inoculation had eliminated these scourges as significant military problems.

Finally, as the most recent therapeutic development, but one which had already made a tentative start before the nineteenth century ended, we have the results of the quest for artificial remedies of a new type, for substances foreign to the body, as were the older drugs, but dealing directly with causes by eliminating the agents of infection, protozoal or bacterial, and not merely palliative of the resulting symptoms. Paul Ehrlich, the man of genius who inspired and led this experimental campaign, called it chemotherapy. It has given us salvarsan, suramin, and mepacrine —mepacrine which made it possible for armies to fight in the malarial swamps of New Guinea, when the Japanese had seized the world's major sources of quinine. And there are signs that it will soon give us remedies for malaria still better than mepacrine. It has given us sulphanilamide and its derivatives, with all that their use has done to weaken the threat of pneumonia, of cerebrospinal fever, of puerperal septicaemia and many other deadly or crippling kinds of infection. Most recently, chiefly through the opportunist genius and the inspired enterprise of our own countrymen, as we may be proud to remember, it has given us the greatest, as yet, of all chemotherapeutic agents, penicillin; and the hunt for other such agents, from other moulds and fungi, capable of stopping bacterial infections which are indifferent to penicillin, is going on now, wherever in the world men can find the means and the opportunity for such beneficent researches. Again I ask you to contrast the helplessness of medicine in the presence of most infections when this century began with its rapidly growing powers of specific healing to-day, and to remember that these still represent only early harvests, from the sowings made by the experimental method in the field of medicine during the latter half of the nineteenth century. Who can appraise the gain to human health and the enrichment of human happiness which the continued growth of such knowledge may bring? The future is bright with promise, indeed, if mankind can be brought to forsake the folly of using the gifts of science for its own destruction.

SCIENCE IN EDUCATION*

M Y SENSE of the honour conveyed by the Master's invitation to me, to speak at the celebration this year of the Foundation of Birkbeck College, was deepened by a glance at the record of those who have spoken here in earlier years to celebrate the same event. It is, indeed, an awe-inspiring succession. The list includes the names of princes and peers, philanthropists and philosophers, poets and politicians; many of the greatest names of the past eighty years, in the service of the Church, of the State, of the Law, are to be found there; service in various connexions to Education is appropriately and widely represented; and there are names well known in Literature and in Science. I found it of some interest to note that, of the seventy-seven Orations hitherto given, seven have been by men whose life's work was in the natural sciences. The proportion does not seem excessive, in view of the expressed purpose of the College, in its first programme, when it was still the London Mechanics' Institution, to offer "education to students in the Principles of the Arts they practise and in the various branches of Science and useful knowledge." We may catch a distant, and, perhaps, an unconscious echo of the functions ascribed to the Royal Society in 1662, in the words of its first Charter—"ad rerum naturalium artiumque scientias . . . promovendas"—"to the advancement of the sciences of natural things and of useful arts." It was rightly emphasized by the historian of this College, the late Cecil Delisle Burns, that it was not technical or trade instruction which was thus early offered here, but education in the scientific principles recognized as underlying the practical employments of these early students. I should like you, on the other hand, to observe, for later reference, that, although the declared aim of the College, even at this larval stage of its existence, was not to give the technical training which an apprenticeship might be expected to provide, it was,

---

* The Foundation Oration delivered at Birkbeck College (University of London) on the occasion of the celebration of the 124th anniversary of the Foundation of the College, 4th May, 1948.

apparently, not concerned to deny, but rather to claim that the more liberal education, which it made available to its students in their spare time, would have a helpful bearing on their daily trades and vocations.

As I indicated a few minutes ago, the record shows that the average frequency, with which this commemorative address has hitherto been given by a worker in the field of the natural sciences, has been once in each eleven years over the whole series; and, since the last of these occasions was twelve years ago, I shall have no sense of an undue urgency, or of thrusting a subject on your notice out of its proper turn, if I present to you to-day some thoughts on the position which may be properly allotted to the natural sciences, under present conditions and under any which we can reasonably foresee, in the educational programme of a College such as this and, indeed, in a liberal scheme of education anywhere in the modern world.

Could we, indeed, find a place more suitable than this for the discussion of such a question? The London Mechanics' Institution, from which this Birkbeck College was in due course to emerge, offered, as we have seen, courses "in the various branches of Science"; and we can further assign to it the role of a veritable pioneer in that direction. For at that time, as Mr. Delisle Burns has reminded us, the study of the natural sciences, apart from mathematics, was still unknown at Oxford and Cambridge, and London had yet no University, or College of University status, to deal with them. I think, indeed, that your College's claim to initiative in this matter will be generally accepted; though I am not quite so sure of a complete unanimity with regard to the merits of the innovation.

For we have long been accustomed to a divided judgment concerning the suitability of the natural sciences for use as an instrument, or a material, of education; and the strength of that section of opinion which ranks them low in the scale of educational values seems to have been subject to rather wide fluctuations, being blown about, apparently, by variable winds of doctrine. At the present moment we may detect a tendency to confusion of the public mind by conflicting advocacies. Before the war had reached its end, powerful pleas had been presented to the Government of the day by the Parliamentary and Scientific Committee, as well as by other students of the situation, urging the need for a greatly accelerated output of scientists in this country, holding degrees from Universities and diplomas from Technical Training Colleges, to meet, in particular, the demands made for such men by British industry and by the Research Organizations supported by British Government Departments. These demands had already been increasing rapidly with the war; their continued growth after its end could be foreseen with confidence, and it could be urged, with a good show of reason, that they would have to be met, if our country was not to find itself at a ruinous disadvantage in competition with others, which had far outstripped us in the provision of such opportunities for scientific and technical training.

Under pressure of such representations the present Government, in December 1945, appointed an important Committee on Scientific Man Power under the chairmanship of Sir Alan Barlow. This Barlow Committee in due course presented a Report calling for a large increase in our national provision of opportunities for higher education and research. These recommendations were not, indeed, restricted to making provision for more students of the natural sciences; but their first concern, naturally and properly, was with the problem submitted to the Committee. As these recommendations become effective, then, the natural sciences, in the number of those studying and teaching them and in the amount of public money devoted to their promotion, are due to acquire a position of increasing importance in the universities. Such an effect will not, indeed, be produced at the expense of the studies concerned with literature, history and the arts, for which an expanded provision was also recommended; but it is not to be denied that the effect of the recommendations will be to give to the natural sciences a growing prominence in the life and the activities of the universities, in comparison with the other faculties of learning.

Such a prospect was bound, I think, by itself to cause a genuine feeling of disquiet among the many who sincerely believe that the studies which, with a convenient ambiguity and looseness of definition, are now termed "the humanities," are alone of value in imparting liberality of culture, skill and precision in the use of language, strength and balance of character, and capacity for the administration of men and affairs. I shall have something further to say concerning the grounds of that belief. For the moment it is sufficient to note that, for one who assumes that the effect, if not the object, of a scientific education is the production of culturally limited, technical specialists, even a proportionate increase in the provision for science in a programme of higher education must be alarming, and especially so, if it is under suspicion of being planned chiefly to meet the competitive needs of industry. Indeed, if such assumptions could be justified, we might all find good grounds for alarm. If a higher education centred on the natural sciences would, in fact, merely train a man to meet the technical demands of a profession; if it would fail, in comparison with other educational disciplines, to qualify him to be a good citizen and an acceptable member of a cultured community; then, indeed, a proportionate increase of scientists among the learned of a nation would inevitably depress that nation's general standard of effective citizenship and culture, or retard its advance in those directions; and, if that were indeed the prospect, there would be the strongest reason for demanding a change of policy.

But before we examine in more detail the credentials of such a belief, we must take note of the fact that, in many minds, the impact of other recent events has appeared to give it a powerful reinforcement. The whole course of the war had witnessed a rapid crescendo in the competitive use of any destructive devices which science could provide. And the use of these was not to be restricted, by the merciful if not wholly logical conventions of earlier times, to destroying only the power of armed forces, but was now to be extended, in contempt of all such conventions, to the ruthless destruction of an enemy nation's people and property, on any scale deemed requisite to reduce it to impotence. The climax, so far, of this sinister development seemed to have been reached in the use of the atomic bomb. This had involved the confirmation of a purely scientific prediction, which represented the furthest advance of evidence and theory in one of the most rapidly progressive branches of physical science. In peace this might well have waited many decades, at least, for its experimental verification; but in a few years of war it had been given practical reality by a secret enterprise of unexampled magnitude. Truly a gigantic achievement of science and technology. The conscience of the world received a shock and its fears for the future of civilization were rightly quickened, when the dropping of the first atomic bomb revealed the tremendous nature of the new power, for good or ill, which the secret use of science in war had put so suddenly into the hands of a humanity unprepared for its reception. "Man," said the Archbishop of Canterbury, in a speech which has been widely quoted, "has made immense advances in scientific knowledge, but he has not made corresponding advances in moral stature."

War had, indeed, revealed and accentuated such a failure of mankind to attain the political wisdom, and the loyalty to principles of morality in dealings between nations, without which we can have no confidence in man's safe employment of any of the resources which science has offered and will continue to offer for his use and enjoyment. It would be gross error, on the other hand, to assume that the disparity to which the Archbishop referred has arisen merely from a reckless pushing of scientific inquiry, and a consequent advance of scientific knowledge, at a speed with which man's moral development cannot reasonably be expected to keep pace. A moment's reflexion on the happenings in the recent war will make it clear that the main, if not the entire cause of the disparity is to be sought in the opposite direction; that it has arisen, in fact, from a relapse of man's moral standards to those of an earlier age, which would have been effective even if science had been at a standstill, or had been kept aloof from the war. For we have to recognize that it was not only, or even mainly, the latest and most advanced discoveries of science, such as the release of nuclear energy, which were perverted to destructive uses in these recent years. On the contrary, the earliest of them all, the kindling and spreading of fire, which man through the ages had been slowly learning to harness and to restrict to a beneficent service, was made again the agent of a destruction as blind and as ruthless as any which our rude ancestors had contrived, but now on a scale of immensely greater magnitude than any which they can have imagined, and, of course, with modern scientific devices to assist in starting and distributing it. If we confine the comparison to the cities of Japan alone, it is certain that a far greater proportion of devastation had already been inflicted on other cities by incendiary bombing from the air, than that which the first two atomic bombs were to cause in Hiroshima and Nagasaki. Of these latter cities something between

36 and 42 per cent was destroyed; but 40 per cent of the capital city of Tokyo and over 57 per cent of the great seaport of Yoko-hama had already been destroyed from the air, and over 95 per cent of the built-up area of Toyama had been obliterated in a single incendiary raid. Figures comparable to these could be quoted for important German cities; but our reactions had been blunted by custom, and the memories of what the Germans had done to some of our own cities had led us to take wholesale incendiarism almost as a normal incident of modern warfare. One would have to be blind, then, to the realities of the situation, to propose that the advance of science should be halted, or delayed, to allow man's moral stature to overtake its responsibility; for on such a principle human culture, with all that it had to offer for the moral development of mankind, should have been stopped short of that earliest of scientific discoveries, which taught primi-tive man the way to light a fire.

It is not difficult, however, to understand the instinctive re-action, to the news of the first atomic bomb, of one who had made up his mind already, that the effect of a scientific education must be to restrict a man's outlook and interests to sordid and material issues, and to blunt his sensibilities to intellectual, aesthetic and moral values. To one who had adopted such a creed, it would, of course, be easy and natural to find in science itself the culprit, and in scientists its agents, for every development which made the last war more horrible than its predecessors. He would find in the atomic bomb, and in the threat for the future of mankind to which many were first awakened by its use, a confirmation of convictions and prejudices already firmly established. While allowing to science its uses as a necessary expedient in war, he would claim, with greater confidence than ever before, that only a humanistic education could furnish the qualities of intellect and character needed now to deal with the national and inter-national problems of peace.

While I have no doubt that there are many who hold such a belief with sincerity, I am as sincerely convinced that it has no firmer basis than confusion of thought and bewilderment. Scientific knowledge cannot, of course, be given practical appli-cation, for good or evil, until the work of the scientist has revealed it; but there is no ground of reason for laying the blame for its perversion to destructive uses on scientists as such, or on the effects

8

of a scientific education. It is a responsibility which we must all accept, as citizens of the belligerent nations, giving a predominant share, indeed, to the aggressors who began such practices, but not seeking to evade our own. In so far as any special and individual responsibility has been involved, it will have to be accepted by the few leaders to whom we, the warring peoples, gave authority for the effective decisions of policy; and it would surely be difficult to make a case for believing that these had had their moral judgment warped, or their moral sense blunted, by scientific training. On the contrary, if it is to be suggested that man's moral inadequacy to deal safely with scientific knowledge is due to any defect in the matter of education, the blame for that state of affairs will have to be laid squarely at the door of the humanistic studies, which have undoubtedly predominated, hitherto, in the education of those to whom we have delegated our responsibility for action in war. I hope, however, that it will be clear that it is no part of my purpose to impute blame to any persons, or to any educational discipline, for a situation at which we all have abundant reason to be alarmed, and not a little, as world citizens, to be ashamed. Nothing, indeed, could be further from my intention. My sole concern is to resist and to repudiate the illogical plausibility, which would call science and scientific education to account for the evil uses which mankind has found for the discoveries of science. It would clearly be no more illogical to blame a humanistic education for all the distortions of historical truth, the misuses of rhetoric, the frenzied appeals to sectarian hatred and political fanaticism, which have been and still are being used to fabricate causes for war, and to inflame the popular will to wage it, with science as a mere, unwilling instrument.

Our discussion has been diverted to a matter which is hardly central or essential to my theme. Even if we have agreed, as I hope we may have done, that there is no reasonable ground for blaming the effects of science as an educational discipline for the abuses of science in war, we do not therewith dismiss as groundless the claims preferred for the superior educational value of the studies dealing with man's activities and creative achievements, in comparison with those directed to the objects and phenomena of nature as a whole. It would not be easy, I think, to find in general principles a warrant for this assumption that study of the works of man must have an educational superiority over study of the works of nature. There are many, however, to whom it does, indeed, appear to be self-evident that only such a humanistic education will provide an adequate discipline for the full development, on the lines best for himself and for the community at large, of all a man's inborn, potential gifts of mind and of character. If you suspect that I exaggerate the fervour of this belief, or the extent to which it has imposed itself upon our general docility, I would only ask you to observe the complacency with which many distinguished scholars disclaim any knowledge or understanding of the mere rudiments of modern science, and to compare this with the shamed reluctance of a comparably eminent student of the sciences to admit such a gap in his own equipment on the side of literature, history, or the fine arts.

Our problem is to consider the true significance of this attitude. We should not hastily accept it, as representing the ripened fruit of age-long experience and wisdom; but we ought not to reject it out of hand, as the mere relic of an outworn tradition. The question is of far too serious a moment to be merely raised and left in suspense, or to be discussed at the level of common-room banter. For, whether we like it or not, there is no escape from the fact that the civilized world, the community in which we have to live and play our parts, is already well over the threshold of the scientific age. Knowledge of the material universe, which is being and will be continuously revealed by science at an increasing rate, is certain to be a growing component, not merely of the working basis of everyday life and experience, but of the very texture of our thoughts. If, therefore, we accept the claim so widely made, for the supremacy of a purely humanistic education as an intellectual and moral discipline in the modern world, we seem to involve ourselves in an admission that the best material for education will be that which keeps the mind aloof and directs its attention away from this main current in the present surge of human civilization.

I do not think that such a conclusion will appear unacceptable to those who adhere to the humanistic faith. On the contrary, I think that I can safely suppose that the belief in the humanistic discipline is often closely allied and in some minds intimately entangled, with a related, though not logically identical doctrine, that education should aim at giving a general culture, and should have no direct relation to the main business of adult life. One has even heard this propounded in the crude form, that the subject of education hardly matters, provided that it is not practically useful. It would be convenient to speak of this as the "cultural" ideal, and to contrast it with the "vocational" ideal in education; but if we are to do so, it is necessary to protect ourselves against being entrapped, by the verbal antithesis, into conceding in advance the point under discussion. We must not allow it to be assumed that an education which is vocational in its aim and content cannot be made, in the truest sense, cultural.* I may remind you that such an assumption would, in fact, be at variance with the principle adopted by this College as the basis of its earliest curriculum. Nor must we forget, on the other hand, that one of the claims made for a humanistic education is to give the best equipment for a range of essentially practical activities; and though this is asserted especially with regard to types of vocation which stand high in general esteem and in the scale of reward—the managerial, administrative, executive and political functions—this must not be allowed to obscure the essential nature of the claim, that an education purely cultural in substance does, for such purposes, produce the best vocational result.

How, then, are we to judge between such rival claims? We can find no answer, in general principles; unless, indeed, we are content to fall into the trap, not unknown, I fear, in educational discussions, of allowing that term to be applied to cherished prejudices. It would not, I think, be difficult to imagine a state of society in which a literary education would be regarded as simply vocational, in comparison with the superior and cultural

---

* In all this discussion of education, indeed, a particular wariness against such verbal traps seems to be advisable. As I have elsewhere pointed out (*Proc. Amer. Philosoph. Soc. of Philadelphia*, Vol. 91, p. 71, 1947), "human" or "humane" knowledge appears to have meant, originally, the secular knowledge won by man's own effort and inquiry, as distinguished from the "divine" knowledge revealed by God through the Church; so that all the natural and mathematical science which then existed would have been included in the new tradition of "humanism." The recent limitation of "humanism" and "humanities" to the study of man's own history and achievements may be legitimate, and even convenient, if the practice, with the ambiguity of modern verbal usage which it entails, is not misused to imply that such studies are alone able to cultivate a "humane" attitude to the world and its problems, in the moral sense of the word. If an alternative nomenclature had been adopted in the first instance, distinguishing "profane" from "sacred" studies, the ambiguity would hardly have arisen.

character of one concerned with such study and enjoyment of nature as might at the time be available. We can even find record of an attitude not widely different from this, in the outburst of a gentleman towards the end of the fifteenth century, which at least makes clear the opinion then held as to the meanly vocational character of what was still the only available scholarship—the Church's Latin, and what knowledge of ancient history and science had come through clerical studies. "To blow a neat blast on a horn," he exclaims, "to understand hunting, to carry a hawk handsomely, that is what becomes the son of a gentleman; but as for book-learning, we should leave that to louts." I believe, indeed, that a great service could be done to the subject of our discussion and to the clarification of our ideas on education in general, if somebody with the requisite equipment of historical scholarship would give us a full and critical history of the changes and the development of educational ideals, and of their effects on educational practice in Western civilization, from ancient Greece to the present day; such a history as, by an impartial and scientific study of the evidence, would lift the subject above the welter of traditional snobberies, of facile dogmatisms, whether reactionary or iconoclastic, in which our discussions of it are apt to flounder. Dr. Trevelyan's "Social History" has, of course, dealt with the development of our English educational institutions, but not, I think, exhaustively with the changes of educational ideals and traditions in the sense which I have in mind.

I need hardly disclaim for myself any qualification for a serious approach to such a theme, even if considerations of time allowed. I venture to predict, however, that such a history would find a whole series of fascinating problems in the almost fantastic inversions of sentiment and attitude over the centuries. Think, for example, of the changes from the sentiment I have quoted, when the literary scholarship of the period was despised as a merely vocational training for the priesthood, to that of more recent times, when the secular scholarship blossoming from the recovered literatures of Greece and Rome had produced a new ideal of cultured leisure for men of birth and property, and when, eventually, Latin and Greek, the "book-learning for louts," had come to be regarded as the basis of the only intellectual discipline to fit man for leadership and easy mastery in the world's affairs. Even to the present day, as we have seen, this newer attitude has, in many minds, been broadened only, and that quite recently, by the admission of other non-scientific studies to the humanistic canon. It would have to be noted, however, that, in the century following that of the revival of ancient learning, there had been a second renascence, a renewal of the investigation of nature by direct observation and experiment, after the age-long restriction to the mere interpretation of such ancient scientific writings as the Church had endorsed. Starting with the books of Copernicus and Vesalius, both published in 1543, the new tradition had passed, through Galileo and other early Italian philosophers, to our own William Gilbert and William Harvey, to the early Fellows of our Royal Society and thus on to Isaac Newton; and the works of all these scientific philosophers, down to Newton's "Principia" in 1687, were written and published in Latin, which they used, however, not as the subject of an aloof scholarship, but as a medium to communicate their discoveries to a Europe in which scientists had come to constitute an international community. One is tempted to wonder whether the lapse of this practice—Newton's "Opticks" (1703) was already published in English—is not to be regretted. Its retention might have had value, not only for the international character which it gave to scientific activity, but for its restrictive effect on the number and verbosity of scientific publications. I believe that our historian would be bound to conclude that science, in those centuries immediately following its rebirth, was an integral part of the new humanism; and one wonders whether he would be able to picture the attitude of these great men, if they could have foreseen our position, centuries later, when science is progressing so fast and so far beyond their furthest horizons, and could have known that, in such a world, many of our ablest students would still have no serious educational contact with knowledge of such a central significance for the world in which they were to live and, perhaps, to find themselves responsible for leadership.

The historical survey would take note of other curious anomalies; of the fact, for example, that an assault, almost as strong as that which has later been needed on behalf of science, had to be made at one period to obtain entry for Greek into the educational fortress which had then come to be occupied by Latin, with a modicum of mathematics, as the almost exclusive garrison. Then, later, came repeated approaches on behalf of the natural sciences to what had become the stronghold of the languages and literature of Greece and Rome. Faraday organised a series of lectures on science and education at the Royal Institution in 1854, one of them being given by Whewell, the Master of Trinity College, Cambridge, whose foible, you may remember, was said to be omniscience. I shall have something to say of his lecture before I conclude. Then, in 1867, there was published a volume of "Essays on a Liberal Education," including a remarkable one by Lord Houghton, scholar and poet, who, discussing the national pride in the character of an English gentleman, derided the assumption that "if in his youth he were taught more or otherwise than he learns at present, some mysterious degradation would inevitably ensue." "Never," continued Lord Houghton, "was there a greater confusion of *post hoc* with *propter hoc* than the theory that his actual excellent characteristics have anything to do with the method of instruction which has been imparted to him"—he was referring, of course, to instruction then practically restricted to the classics. Later he lays positive emphasis on "the scientific method which is above measure valuable as a training of the adolescent mind. To lay early the foundation of certainty is to build up the man of principle and conviction, and has a moral purpose beyond any intellectual gain to be derived from the distinctions and functions of language." In the 1870's and 80's came T. H. Huxley's lectures and addresses, abundantly worth reading still, not only for the power with which they urge the value of science in a well-planned curriculum, but for the use of his mother tongue, by this man of scientific education, with a precise economy and a vivid artistry unsurpassed by any writer of English prose in his generation. Yet only the surface of our national complacency seemed to have been stirred, and during the first world war a "Committee on the Neglect of Science" was formed, on which men of science were joined by representatives of literature and scholarship, such as the late Poet Laureate, Dr. Bridges, and Dr. Macan, then Master of University College, Oxford, under the chairmanship of the third Lord Rayleigh. Notable speeches were made and recorded at a meeting of this Committee held in 1917. Dr. Macan, himself a distinguished Hellenist, protested that "those who like ourselves are demanding an extension of scientific education in this country, are working in the true interests of Hellenism and the spirit of Ancient Greece." The ancient Greeks, indeed, would surely have ridiculed the idea that the only cultural basis for their education was to be found in the records of earlier civilizations, long extinct, instead of in their own literary and scientific achievements. At the end of that war, in 1918, an official Committee appointed by the Prime Minister, Mr. Lloyd George, under the chairman-ship of Sir J. J. Thomson, made strong and moderate recom-mendations on the position of science in the educational system, which undoubtedly had an effect on the curriculum in the secondary schools. And now, after the second world war, we have had Sir Alan Barlow's Committee, which I mentioned earlier, dealing with the need for a proportionate expansion of the opportunities for scientific education in the Universities.

And, it may be asked, does not all this show that the battle has been won? Are you not flogging a dead horse? And I must reply, "No, I do not think so; not until we can be assured of a sincere recognition of the high educational value of science, as an essential constituent of a liberal culture and as an intellectual and moral discipline". There are signs, indeed, and most welcome ones, of a movement in that direction. Only last year the Master of the Rolls, Lord Greene, in his Presidential address to the Classical Association, advocated the inclusion of science as a constituent of a special course of humane studies, which he desired to see instituted in schools. On the other hand, I shall not believe that the horse is really dead, while statements are made, by men who have a right to be heard on educational matters, which still assume a peculiar value for literary studies, and especially for the classics, as a training for the mind, and deny, either directly, or by implication, any comparable value for science. My distinguished friend, Mr. R. A. Butler, for example, preceded me here three years ago, and I have nothing but admiration for the Address which he gave. Two years earlier, however, when he was still Minister for Education, even Mr. Butler was reported to have made public profession of his faith, that "a good grasp of Latin would enable the possessor to take the internal combustion engine in his stride." There could surely be no better example of Lord Houghton's *post hoc propter hoc* than the implied assumption, that an able boy, if, in spite of headmasterly enticements, his mind had been disciplined and exercised by science and engineering, would not be able similarly to take Latin in his stride.

I am afraid that this discussion of my subject has, so far, been rather provocative, though in the sense, I hope, of stirring thought rather than of raising antagonism. In the short time left to me, I should like to make brief mention of some more constructive ideas.

1. According to my own belief and experience, scientists, as a body, do not make any exclusive claim for the value of science as an educational medium. They claim only an abandonment of traditional assumptions as to the exclusive merits of other disciplines. I think that, as a body, they understand and share the general concern that the claims of science to a growing share in educational influence, in an increasingly scientific civilization, shall not threaten such encroachment as to produce a new imbalance in education. I think that we ought to agree that it should be a major concern of our policy for higher education, to maintain and strengthen contacts, and to build new bridges of common interest, between those who approach learning and the achievements of the human mind from the literary and the scientific aspects. For that purpose I would urge that a course in the general history of science, dealing with the story, through the ages, of man's discoveries, of the growth of his knowledge and the development of his theories concerning the nature of the material universe, would be worthy of special consideration. I thought that there might be a trace of novelty in such a plea, till I found that Whewell, the Master of Trinity, in the course arranged by Faraday in 1854, had devoted the whole of his lecture to advocating it. I must be content to be less than a century behind him. Oxford has a Reader in the subject, Cambridge a course of lectures, and London, at University College, has already created a Chair from which Professor Dingle deals with it. I should like to see it made an obligatory subject of examination, for an entrance scholarship to a University in any faculty; and it seems to me to have a peculiar fitness for Lord Greene's proposed course of humane studies in the schools.

2. If science is to take its proper place in a liberal education, it must so be taught as to give it its greatest cultural value.

It is not to be doubted that the facts of science can so be presented as to impart little of its potential value as a mental discipline, in quickening and exercising the faculties of exact observation and logical reasoning, and as a moral discipline, in creating the ideal of a patient devotion to the pursuit and the progressive revelation of objective truth, in freedom from every kind of prejudice and preconception. All this can be missed and the data of science, if badly presented, can certainly be made as intellectually deadening as can those of classical or historical scholarship, under like conditions.

3. And, lastly, I should like to say a word concerning the ill-repute, with many educational authorities, of the vocational aspect of education. We shall have to beware, I think, of allowing traditions and ideals, derived from a period when the accepted object of higher education was to provide a cultural occupation for the leisure of a privileged few, to retain their influence on policy, into a period when access to higher education is being offered to all who can benefit by it. Can we be sure that the influence of this tradition, spreading downwards as such traditions always will, has not already had a harmful effect? When the people of a country have observed, through more than one generation, the respect received by the man of leisure and the influence which he wields, and have compared it with the relatively small repute which is won by even the devoted industry of one who needs to work; when an ideal of education, as primarily concerned with a cultural filling for leisure, has filtered down even to the primary schools; when the value of science has been widely represented as due to its power of reducing work and lengthening leisure; is it a matter for surprise that less work and more leisure, with more pay to fill it agreeably, should become a dangerously prevalent ambition? It seems to me that we who are concerned for the proper place of science in education may well find matter for careful thought in this problem. Educational ideals are apt to arise and educational policies to be first developed at the university level. And I venture to suggest that the ideal, still widely accepted, of keeping education broadly unvocational to as late a stage as possible, may well require to be carefully scrutinized, with regard to its fitness for our modern world.

Is it not possible, even likely, that, with the majority of

students, the easiest way to the awakening of intellectual ambition, of that genuine hunger to know and to learn which is education's finest achievement, is to be found through a vocational course, if that can so be planned as to provide an effective stimulus and discipline for the mind? We come back, Master, to the original aims of this College, to offer "education to students in the Principles of the Arts they practice." The old apprenticeship of those days, the true secondary education then for so many, with all the joy of the good craftsman in his handiwork which it created, has almost passed away. And surely it should be one of the chief aims of our educational plans and ambitions to find something which will worthily replace it, in an industry which science has made so mechanical and has so organized that the task is ever more specialized and divided. I do not believe that we can achieve that purpose by assuming that the main task of science, in our modern civilization, is progressively to reduce work, and that the consequent aim of education should be to provide for a corresponding expansion of leisure. Let the application of science, by all means, reduce to elimination the need for sordid drudgery; but let us take as our ideal, and as a basis of our policy, an education, with science as a natural component, which will ennoble work, will make still possible an intelligent joy in its performance, and will give it again the first place in a man's or a woman's interest, whether it be done in field or factory, in laboratory or library, or even at the domestic hearth. If that could be achieved, if the thirst for knowledge and the enjoyment of mental activity could be thus widely awakened, I believe that a worthy use, in leisure, of what other resources education can provide, would be a more natural consequence, than from a curriculum making leisure's occupation its first care. If such an educational ideal is to be made effective, I believe that its flame will have to be kindled and tended and its light radiated from university centres. And it seems to me that it would be especially congenial to the earliest traditions of this College, and to their noblest developments throughout the century and a quarter of its history, that it should still be a leading centre of such radiation.

ACCIDENT
AND OPPORTUNISM
IN MEDICAL RESEARCH*

M Y TITLE speaks of accident and opportunism, and it hardly requires to be said that the two must go together if accident is to have any value, if it, indeed, is to be anything but a hindrance to research of any kind. Perhaps it is one of the important qualifications for success in research that a man should know, by the subconscious reasoning which we call instinctive judgment, whether what appears to be an accident, a phenomenon presenting itself quite unexpectedly, is just a nuisance, the result of some trivial error, so that the further study of it will lead to nothing but waste of time and energy, or whether on the other hand it offers a possible clue to some new discovery of real importance, which ought to be followed even at the cost, perhaps, of a diversion from the original objective. The same idea has often been expressed by saying that accidents fruitful in discovery happen only to those who deserve them—to those, we may say, in whom a natural aptitude has been reinforced by stored and ripened experience, so that a trained alertness, which does not distract the attention or weaken its concentration on the chosen objective, holds the mind ready to pounce on an unexpected opportunity. If we were called upon to construct a scale of values for the different kinds of scientific research, we might feel bound to accord the highest rank to the kind of investigation which can be systematically planned in advance, such as one which sets out to interpret by mathematical analysis a set of astronomical or physical data; but accidents of the useful kind have sometimes been effective even in attracting and, as it were, refocussing the attention of some of the greatest of mathematical theorists. You will remember how Archimedes, the greatest mathematician of his own and one of the greatest, I suppose, of all ages, found the clue not only to the solution of the practical problem concerning the

* Being the Popular Lecture delivered on 2nd July at the Annual Meeting of the British Medical Association, Cambridge, 1948.

adulteration of the gold used for the king's crown, but to one of the fundamental laws of hydrostatics, in a sufficiently common-place accident—the overflowing of his bath when he lowered his body into the water. Some nineteen centuries later the young Isaac Newton, driven home to Woolsthorpe from Cambridge by the arrival here of the plague, had been directing his astonishing powers to an attempt to discover a cause for the orbital motion of the moon round the earth and of the planets round the sun. Remembering later those years when he was yet only twenty-three to twenty-four years old, he wrote of himself: "I was in the prime of my age for invention and minded mathematics and philosophy more than at any time since"; and on that alert and receptive mind the sight of an apple falling from a tree in the Woolsthorpe garden acts like a trigger, and it comes to him in a flash that the gravity which pulls the apple to earth is holding the moon in its orbit; and he plunges into the calculations which, when some twenty years later they were given to the world in the *Principia*, were so completely to reshape men's ideas of the universe.

I could find other examples, if we required them, of the way in which theoretical and experimental investigators in the fields of pure physics and chemistry have on occasion been able to take advantage of accidental observations, to make great new advances in their various special fields. Accident certainly played some part, though probably not so great a part as popular rumour has sometimes suggested, in those great discoveries, a little over half a century ago, of the X-rays by Röntgen and of the radioactivity of uranium by Becquerel, which together contributed so much to the launching of physics into its new era. Certainly they did not belong to the same class as the discoveries which most people were expecting to arise, from the natural and straightforward development of the physical knowledge of the day. I have a very clear recollection of the interest which they aroused, when the news of them first came to Cambridge in my second and third undergraduate years. And, of course, none of us had then any inkling of the enormous expansion of knowledge for which dis-coveries such as these were to provide the points of origin, or of the whole armoury of physical resources which would thus be brought to the service of medicine. This is even now receiving a reinforcement of yet unmeasured magnitude from the forward leap which knowledge in nuclear physics has made in these recent years, and on the uses of which so much of the world's hopes and so much of its fears are now centred.

MEDICAL RESEARCH

The mention of such applications to the service of medicine brings me at last to the subject of my paper—the part played by accident and opportunism in medical research, which is the field of scientific activity of which I can speak from some personal experience, and the one which we may regard as specially appropriate to this occasion. Medical research as we know it to-day has spread its tentacles widely, and there is hardly any branch of experimental science now which may not find itself seized and pressed into the service, constrained to contribute from some angle, either directly or from a distance, to the scientific basis of modern medical knowledge and practice. That, however, is a very recent development; modern medical research as an experimental science, or a varied group of experimental scientific disciplines, had not begun a hundred years ago, and was only just beginning to get really under way at the beginning of the present century. Yet medical knowledge was making important advances at the end of the eighteenth and in the first half of the nineteenth century at the hands of the great physicians of those days, who used to the full the opportunities which they encountered by accident in their practice, enabling them to observe the regular recurrences of symptoms and conditions which others had passed unnoticed. Thus the immunity from smallpox of those who had infected their hands with the cowpox appears to have been a matter of common belief with the dairymaids and other country folk, among whom Edward Jenner practised in Gloucestershire. None of the other medical men of the neighbourhood, however, had observed the fact, much less recognized its significance; they even threatened, jestingly we may hope, to expel Jenner from their Convivio-Medical Club if he continued to bore them with such nonsense. So he waited for many years, accumulating data as accident gave him opportunity, until at length in 1796 he followed the advice given long before by his friend John Hunter, and tried the experiment, inoculating a boy with cowpox and, when that had passed, proving him to be completely refractory to inoculation with smallpox. Jenner, then, in the light of later developments, may be regarded as having found already, long in advance of his time, the bridge between the method which waits for opportunities of observation to be provided by nature and encountered by accident, and that which puts a possibility to deliberate test, under the critical and controlled conditions of experiment. And I propose now to bring to your special notice a few out of a large number of possible instances, of the way in which the use of opportunity provided by accident has made contributions, some of them of the very highest importance, to the progress of medical knowledge by research, even in its more recent and still flourishing experimental period.

This revolutionary change in the methods of advancing medical knowledge began, as I have suggested, in the second half of the nineteenth century; and if anybody was asked to name the important factors of its beginning and its promotion he could not fail to give to the work and the discoveries of Louis Pasteur, and to the whole science of bacteriology which grew out of them, a leading place among these factors. Everybody knows that it is to the discoveries of Pasteur that we can trace the first clear recognition of living and self-multiplying micro-organisms, yeasts and bacteria, as responsible for the familiar processes of fermentation and putrefaction, and then for diseases transmitted by infection and contagion. I do not think, however, that it is so generally known that accident—a whole series, indeed, of accidental and extraneous circumstances—played a very prominent part in engaging and focussing Pasteur's attention for the remainder of his life on studies which were widely divergent from the line of his original scientific interests and activities. For Pasteur began his scientific career as a mineralogist and a crystallographer. His first great discovery concerned the crystallography of the two isomeric forms of tartaric acid and revealed their true relations to racemic acid. It was he who discovered that the two forms which, in solution, rotate the plane of polarized light in opposite directions, have crystals with forms related to one another as that of an asymmetrical object is related to its image in a mirror—a discovery as fundamental to organic chemistry as to crystallography, and one which might well, one thinks, have occupied the rest of his life in its direct development. But a mould, a *Penicillium*, grew by accident on his solution containing both the forms of a tartrate; and Pasteur found that, as it grew, it selectively used and destroyed only the form producing right-handed rotation of the plane of a polarized beam, so that the left-rotating tartrate remained. And then, with his mind thus rendered alert to the new idea of a selective fermentation as due to the action of living and multiplying organisms, Pasteur was given additional stimulus and opportunity in that direction by his appointment to a chair of chemistry at Lille, where practical problems of fermentation in the local distilling industry were waiting for his ripening genius to begin the great clarification. And soon his success led to appeals to him to investigate the causes of the variable results encountered in the fermentative production of vinegar and in the brewing of beer, and he was summoned then to deal with the diseases of wine in his own native countryside; and in every case he was able to identify and to separate the micro-organisms responsible for the desired fermentation, and to show the way to eliminate those which diverted it harmfully. And then, of course, his success with the diseases of wine involved him in insistent pleas that he would direct his researches to the elimination of the infectious disease known as "pebrine" from silkworms. And thus the train was laid for the great revolution in the pathology and eventually in the treatment of infectious diseases, through the further work of Pasteur himself and his immediate pupils in Paris, of Koch in Germany, of Lister in this country, and of all the great host of their disciples and followers throughout the world, right down to the present day, who have caught and carried forward the flame first kindled from the interest of a man of genius in the crystallography of the tartaric acids, and in the accidentally observed effect of a mould which grew on them.

BEGINNING OF ENDOCRINOLOGY

As another leading factor in the great change which has come over the whole aspect of medical knowledge and research we should certainly mention the rise of experimental physiology and, later, of biochemistry. And among the special fields of investigation in the general domain of these, which have had a specially direct influence on knowledge of diseases and their treatment, we might well mention those concerned with the hormones and the vitamins. And here again, if we look at the beginnings of experimental activity in both these fields, we shall find the exploitation of happy accident playing a part of real importance.

The real beginning of scientific endocrinology, the study of the internal secretions or hormones, may be found, I suppose, in the brilliant use which great English physicians of the middle of the nineteenth century made of their opportunities, presented by accident, for accurate observations at the bedside and in the post-mortem room: when Thomas Addison described the malady known by his name and recognized its regular association with destructive disease of the suprarenal gland, and when William Gull described myxoedema as a kind of adult cretinism and traced it to atrophy of the thyroid gland. But nobody in 1889 had any idea that the much commoner disease, diabetes mellitus, had any connection with the defect of a gland or the lack of an internal secretion. In that year Professor von Mering, of Strasbourg, asked his colleague Professor Minkowski, to remove the pancreas from a dog by operation in order that they might study the absorption of fat from the intestine in the absence of that gland*. So, purely by accident, it was discovered that the dog without a pancreas showed an abnormal hunger and thirst and passed large volumes of urine, which Minkowski found to be loaded with glucose. Naturally he turned aside to investigate the condition more closely, and point by point he found it to correspond with a severe diabetes mellitus, as this had long been known in the human patients whom it afflicted. But more than thirty years were to pass before this discovery was made fully effective for medical practice by the determined enterprise of two young Canadians, Banting and Best, who, after many experienced investigators had failed, demonstrated the possibility of preparing the missing hormone, insulin, from the pancreas and therewith changed completely the prospect of the sufferer from diabetes. More than that, I think that it cannot be doubted that the stimulus due to Banting and Best's success was an important factor in the astonishing advance which research began at once and continues still to achieve over this whole field of

---

* Different accounts of this incident vary in detail. It seems to be certain, however, that Minkowski offered to do the operation, and that v. Mering, incredulous of its success, went on leave as soon as it had been performed; and that Minkowski then found that, as an unexpected result, the animal had become severely diabetic.

knowledge of the endocrine glands and their hormones. Let me mention just one item. But a few years ago the disease known as pernicious anaemia, or sometimes as Addison's anaemia, was as completely beyond the reach of effective remedy as diabetes had earlier been, when a team of physicians in Boston (Mass.) discovered that a hormone could be prepared from the liver, by the use of which the prospect of the sufferer from pernicious anaemia has been transformed as completely as that of the sufferer from diabetes by insulin. The senior member of that Boston team, Professor Minot, is himself a sufferer from diabetes, and insulin had come just in time to save him from a premature death, and to fit him to take a leading part in the discovery which is now saving others from pernicious anaemia. Is it fanciful, then, to find in Minkowski's enlightened use of the opportunity which accident offered him in 1889 the real starting-point for work which has now led to the effective treatment of more than one disease, regarded till a few years ago as beyond any hope of remedy?

NUTRITION AND BIOCHEMISTRY

There has been a good deal of discussion, in an entirely friendly spirit, concerning the real starting point of the researches which led to the recognition of the vitamins and thus to the specific and effective treatment or prevention of a number of other formerly mysterious diseases now known to be due to the lack of one or another of these trace-constituents of a normal diet. There is one accidental observation, used to remarkable purpose by the late Sir Frederick Gowland Hopkins, which must, I think, be regarded as the first link in a chain of discoveries by which that great investigator was led to his first recognition of the factors which we have come to call the vitamins. One student in Hopkins's early advanced class at Cambridge, the late John Mellanby, who was long afterwards the distinguished occupant of the Oxford Chair of Physiology in succession to Sherrington, was curiously unable to obtain the colour reaction for proteins which a certain Adamkiewicz had described; and Hopkins himself found that, with the particular bottle of acetic acid on Mellanby's shelf, it was indeed unobtainable, though that from all the other bottles in the laboratory gave it readily. He did not put the matter aside as one of those queer anomalies and content himself with telling Mellanby to borrow the reagent from his neighbour; he recognized, with his remarkable instinct, that here was something of potential importance, and with the assistance of another member of the class, S. W. Cole, he immediately began the investigation which led them to the discovery that the reaction was due to glyoxylic acid, which almost all specimens of acetic acid contain as an impurity. Then, with a more effective reagent, they were able to isolate the constituent of proteins giving this and another well-known colour reaction, and to identify it as a new amino-acid, tryptophane. And then Hopkins undertook experiments to determine the degree to which each of the different amino-acids which had then been identified, tryptophane among them, was a necessary constituent of a diet for maintenance and growth; and thus he was led further to the discovery that young rats could not grow, or even maintain their weight, on food made up from all the *known* constituents of a complete diet in abundance, if these had been elaborately purified. So it was made clear that there were unknown factors of a normal diet, minute in quantity but essential to make the food adequate in quality for normal nutrition; and biochemistry was launched upon what soon became a worldwide expedition of research, still in progress, in pursuit of the vitamins.

Many of you, I think, will have heard of "Ringer's solution" —a watery solution of salts in carefully adjusted proportions, with which the late Dr. Sidney Ringer was able to maintain the heart removed from the body of a dead frog in vigorously beating activity for hours. Ringer was a physician to University College Hospital, and, in such time as he could spare from his practice, one of the pioneers of pharmacological research in this country. In his early experiments he had found that a solution containing only pure sodium chloride, common salt, in the proportion in which it is present in the serum of frog's blood, would keep the beat of the heart in action only for a short time, after which it weakened and soon stopped. And then suddenly the picture changed: apparently the same pure salt solution would now maintain the heart in vigorous activity for many hours. Ringer was puzzled, and thought for a time that the difference must be due to a change in the behaviour of the frog's heart with the season of the year—until he discovered what had really happened. Being busy with other duties, he had entrusted the preparation of his solutions to his laboratory boy, one Fielder; and as Fielder himself, whom I knew as an ageing man, explained to me, he didn't see the point of spending all that time distilling water for Dr. Ringer, who wouldn't notice any difference if the salt solution was made up with water straight out of the tap. But, as we have seen, Ringer did notice the difference; and when he discovered what had happened he did not merely become angry and insist on having distilled water for his saline solution; he took full advantage of the opportunity which accident had thus offered him and soon discovered that water from the tap, supplied then to North London by the New River Company, contained just the right small proportion of calcium ions to make a physiologically balanced solution with his pure sodium chloride; and when, guided by further analysis, he had also added the correct small proportion of a potassium salt, Ringer's solution was complete, and with the later modifications which Locke, Tyrode, and others introduced to make it suitable for the tissues of other animals, it has become an essential reagent for everyday use in an immense range of medical and biological research procedures.

ADRENALINE AND ACETYLCHOLINE

Some fifteen years later another observation, also of far-reaching effect on the progress of physiology, was made in the same laboratory at University College in circumstances which, if not entirely accidental, had at least something of that character. Dr. George Oliver, a physician of Harrogate, employed his winter leisure in experiments on his family, using apparatus of his own devising for clinical measurements. In one such experiment he was applying an instrument for measuring the thickness of the radial artery; and, having given his young son, who deserves a special memorial, an injection of an extract of the suprarenal gland, prepared from material supplied by the local butcher, Oliver thought that he detected a contraction or, according to some who have transmitted the story, an expansion of the radial artery. Whichever it was, he went up to London to tell Professor Schäfer what he thought he had observed, and found him engaged in an experiment in which the blood pressure of a dog was being recorded; found him, not unnaturally, incredulous about Oliver's story and very impatient at the interruption. But

Oliver was in no hurry, and urged only that a dose of his supra-renal extract, which he produced from his pocket, should be injected into a vein when Schäfer's own experiment was finished. And so, just to convince Oliver that it was all nonsense, Schäfer gave the injection, and then stood amazed to see the mercury mounting in the arterial manometer till the recording float was lifted almost out of the distal limb.

Thus the extremely active substance formed in one part of the suprarenal gland, and known as adrenaline, was discovered. And in due course there came to light the curious correspondence between the effects produced by this potent substance and those produced by nerves of the so-called sympathetic system; and Professor T. R. Elliott, then a postgraduate research student in Cambridge, was led to make the brilliant suggestion that these sympathetic nerves produce their effects by liberating small quan-tities of adrenaline at the points where they end in contact with muscle fibres and gland cells. Some ten years later it came to my notice, by sheer accident, that a particular extract of the drug known as ergot of rye exhibited a curious and very potent type of activity. With the co-operation of my chemical colleague at the time, Dr. Ewins, the substance responsible was isolated from the ergot extract and identified as the acetic-ester of the base choline, acetylcholine. And when the actions of this came to be examined in detail they showed as suggestive a correspondence to the effects of other nerves, as those of adrenaline had shown to the effects of the sympathetic nerves in particular. At that time there was no reason at all to believe that acetylcholine was a natural constituent of the animal and human body; but my late colleague, Dr. Dudley, and I found it there some fifteen years later, again by accident, when we were looking for something else. And meanwhile my friend of many years, Professor Otto Loewi, then of Graz but now in New York, by experiments of a most elegant simplicity had directly demonstrated, in confir-mation of Elliott's much earlier suggestion, that impulses passing down the fibres of different nerves to the frog's heart do in fact produce their effects by liberating, at the junctions of the nerve with the muscle fibres, one or the other of two substances; and these two substances were found to be identical with adrenaline and acetylcholine in all the properties for which they could be tested. And further developments, in which I have again taken a part, entitle me to believe that, even at this moment, impulses passing down nerve fibres are liberating tiny charges of acetylcholine where these fibres end in the muscles of my tongue, my lips, my larynx and my diaphragm, and are throwing these into the complicated and varying patterns of speech, which, I hope, contrives none the less to be reasonably articulate.

HISTAMINE AND PENICILLIN

The intimacy of direct experience may to some extent justify this mention of incidents involving my own activities, alongside the examples of the far-reaching importance of the part which accident may play in medical research, which I have cited earlier. If further excuse is needed, I may plead that the function of acetylcholine as a transmitter of nervous effects figured prominently in a discussion meeting held here yesterday in one of the scientific sections of the British Medical Association. There is even something of the nature of an accident in the fact that this morning another of the sections had a discussion on a novel group of remedies called "Antihistamine substances"; for histamine is another base which came to my notice by accident, some forty years ago, as accounting for the special activity of another kind of extract from the same curious drug, ergot of rye. When histamine had thus been isolated and identified by my late colleague, Professor George Barger, it proved to have an action reproducing most of the symptoms characteristic of an "anaphylactic" or "allergic" reaction—a type of reaction which will be familiar to most of you in the special forms of hay-fever, nettle-rash, and some forms of asthma. Then I had another stroke of luck. I was studying a rather weak activity of a similar kind which fresh blood serum exhibited, when it was applied to strips of involuntary muscle taken from a dead guinea-pig; and I suddenly encountered a strip of this tissue from one particular guinea-pig which responded with a contraction of peculiar violence when it was treated with a mere trace of horse serum, though it behaved quite normally in the presence of blood serum from other animals —cat, dog, rabbit, sheep, or man. And it occurred to me that many guinea-pigs in that laboratory were used for testing the strength of antitoxic horse serum, and that an economically minded colleague might have provided me with a survivor from such a test. The verification of that suspicion gave us a new idea about the meaning of the anaphylactic or allergic condition; but it took many years more, and a great deal of work in many laboratories in different countries, before we were able to establish the fact that histamine is a natural constituent of most cells of the living body, which is normally held harmless and inactive in their interior, but is released, so as to produce its characteristic effects, if the living cells come into contact with some substance from a plant or animal—grass pollen, scurf from a skin, and so forth—to which they have become abnormally sensitive or allergic. And now, here in Cambridge, only this morning, we have been discussing the action of "antihistamines"—substances for which it is claimed that they relieve the symptoms by preventing the action of histamine, when this is set free by the effect, on allergic cells, of the substances for which they have acquired a specific sensitiveness.

There is one more example which I must mention, even if only because it will certainly, and most properly, be already in the minds of many of you—the discovery of penicillin. The contamination of a bacterial culture growing upon a plate of solid nutritive medium, by the spore of a mould falling on it while the cover is removed for examination, must be a frequent and usually no more than a mildly annoying incident of bacteriological practice. It was the chance coincidence of three conditions which made its occurrence on a particular plate in 1929 the starting point of a discovery of first-rate importance. (1) The contaminating spore was that of one particular mould species, *Penicillum notatum*; (2) the culture on the plate was that of a staphylococcus, susceptible to the restraining effect of an antibacterial agent which this mould produced; and (3), most important of all, the worker concerned was Professor Alexander Fleming, with the eye of a medical naturalist, alert to detect the unusual phenomenon of a kind of halo around the spot where the mould colony grew, free from colonies of the staphylococcus which grew abundantly over the rest of the plate. Sir Alexander Fleming, as you know, picked off the mould colony and cultivated it in a broth, and found that the broth contained an antibacterial agent which he named penicillin. Then, as happened with Minkowski and the pancreatic hormone, neither Fleming nor anyone else for some years could hold out any hope of the chemical isolation or even of a substantial purification of penicillin, to say nothing of its eventual production in a form and in a quantity enabling its therapeutic possibilities to be critically tested. Such a possibility had in fact been practically written off the account and almost forgotten until, like Banting and Best with insulin, Sir Howard Florey and his chemical collaborators took it up with determined energy and with brilliant and resourceful enterprise; and now the research chemists and the organized therapeutic industry of half the world have combined to exploit and develop this gift of an alert opportunism and to make it a practical reality for human need. And the chemists have isolated several penicillins, determined their constitutions, and even made one of them by synthesis. And this success has had value not merely for its own sake; it has opened up a most hopeful vista of other and perhaps equally important discoveries in the same field, streptomycin, chloromycetin, and others yet to come.

Of course there are plenty of other instances to be found, of opportunity coming to an attentive worker in research, through what we have to regard as chance or accident; and, apart from the many which could be collected, there must be innumerable cases which will never be recognized, because no record of them has been preserved. I hope, however, that my choice of a subject and citation of examples will not bring me under the suspicion of suggesting that accident is the principal factor of success in research of any kind, or of medical research in particular. Accidents of the kind which we have been discussing do not, in fact, happen to the merely fanciful speculator, who waits on chance to provide him with inspiration. They come rather to him who, while continuously busy with the work of research, does not close his attention from matters outside this principal aim and immediate objective, but keeps it alert to what unexpected observation may have to offer. I certainly do not believe that any research of permanent value is done, or any discovery of importance soundly established, without a great deal of hard, systematic, and conscientious work.

Then I should not like to be misunderstood as suggesting that mankind would have been left in permanent ignorance of any of the items of scientific knowledge, great and small, which I have cited, through default of the accidents which were in fact associated with their discovery. If Archimedes' bath had failed to overflow, or the falling apple to catch Newton's attention, the principles which they gave to the world would not have remained hidden for ever, and probably not for long. We know in fact that Hooke, Wren, and Halley were actually competing in speculation about an inverse-square law of gravity and the moon's orbit, without being able to calculate the relation; and that it was the news, indeed, of such an approach to its independent discovery which acted as a stimulus to Newton, leading him to publish at last what he had known in principle and worked upon intermittently for over twenty years. We cannot be so certain in other cases, but it does not seem likely that the effects of removing the pancreas, or of injecting a suprarenal extract into a vein, would have remained very long unknown, even if von Mering had not called on Minkowski to perform the one for another purpose, or if Oliver had not goaded a reluctant and sceptical Schäfer into trying the other. Incidents of the kind which I have described may greatly advance the date of a discovery, or may associate it with the name of a particular investigator, but I do not believe that they will ever produce discoveries which would not eventually be made without them. They may provide, however, touches of highlight in the varied landscape of science, of decoration to its solid building, or of light relief to the more serious drama of its normal and logical advancement. And if they have thus lent something of life and colour and everyday interest to an hour of talk about medical research, they have helped me to achieve a large part of my intention.

MEDICAL RESEARCH AS
AN AIM IN LIFE*

I AM proud of the honour you have done me in inviting me to address your Royal Medical Society with its long record and ancient traditions. Of two other Chartered Royal Societies with which I have had some connexion, the Royal Society of London for the Advancement of Natural Knowledge, to give it its full title, which by right of seniority has come to be known as *the* Royal Society, antedated your Society in foundation by some seventy-six years; on the other hand the Royal Society of Medicine, centred also in London, even if we date it from the foundation of its principal constituent, the Royal Medico-Chirurgical Society, has to admit to being your junior by about sixty years. I like the ripeness and dignity of old traditions; we may sometimes need them in these days as a check on haste and exuberance; but we all know their detrimental possibilities, if they are just blindly worshipped, without any serious attempt to blend and harmonize them with healthy and necessary modern development. When, therefore, I was invited to address your ancient Society, I thought it might be appropriate for me to speak to you about something which, as a consciously-recognized development of medical activities, is a comparative novelty—medical research, which happens to be also the only kind of medical activity about which I am entitled to speak from first-hand knowledge.

The half-century of which the end is now not far ahead of us has seen a great widening of the range of careers open to one who is newly graduated or qualified in medicine. His choice among these may seem to present a peculiar difficulty at the present time, when the framework of medical practice, and especially of general, family practice, has been subjected to so sudden and so drastic a strain of reconstruction, of which the ultimate effects cannot as yet be predicted with any confidence. I suspect that some of those who, till the last few years, might have regarded general practice as their obvious aim, providing them with the

* A Lecture delivered to the Royal Medical Society, Edinburgh, 21st January, 1949.

128

kind of opportunity for which they felt themselves to be naturally fitted, in the social setting most congenial to their tastes and aptitudes, may now be giving a closer consideration to alternative careers, such as preventive medicine, public health administration, or one of the various lines of academic or professional activity in which a medical man can now earn a modest remuneration, while using his special training for the benefit of the community. And among such other possibilities will be a life in which medical research provides a major interest, even if it does not constitute the main claim to a livelihood.

Recent years, indeed, have seen a remarkable development of the general interest in medical research as an activity to be encouraged, and a rapid extension in more than one direction, of its recognized scope. On the one side there has been a noteworthy growth, or perhaps one should rather say a conspicuous revival, of our perception of the extent to which the direct study of disease in man can partake of the nature of a genuine scientific research, to the great benefit of the advance of medical knowledge. My late distinguished friend Sir Thomas Lewis devoted much of the energies of his later years to a veritable mission, in which he urged two different aspects of this development upon our notice. On the one hand, he insisted with a burning conviction that research in clinical medicine must be regarded as a distinct and independent branch of experimental science, having its own methods and its own special technical equipment, as clearly separate from those of the laboratory disciplines of physiology, pharmacology and pathology, with their appeal by analogy to experiments on the lower animals, as these were from the methods special to other departments of science. It seems to me likely that Lewis was basing that claim largely on experience of his own brilliant success in the use of the experimental method for the analysis of symptoms which disease had produced. He seemed to me to underestimate the impediments to its use, on man himself, for the study of other and very important aspects of a disease, such as its aetiology, involving deliberate attempts to produce it, and therapeutics, involving the trial of new treatments. There is a clear case, I think, for getting all the accessible information on such matters from experiments on the lower animals, in the laboratories of pathology and chemotherapy, before seeking a final extension of some of this knowledge to the case of man, which may necessitate and justify experimental confirmation and trials on human patients, when the safety of the trials and the co-operation of the subjects are assured. Lewis was at least equally concerned to establish a tradition for clinical research as a whole-time career in itself and to get rid of a convention which had long made it depend, for its opportunities, mostly on the mixed experience of a visiting and consulting physician, and for its financial support on his private practice. In this direction I think that Lewis was adding the impulse of his convincing advocacy and his inspiring leadership to a current of opinion which had already been gathering energy and volume for several decades on the European continent, and in the United States of America. Its vigorous flow in this country could hardly, I think, have been long delayed, in any case; but Lewis had every good reason for wishing to accelerate it.

When I said that medical research had been extending its recognized scope in more than one direction, I had in mind the obvious fact that, even before the beginning of this outburst of interest and this organization of activity in directly clinical research on disease, there had been, on the other hand, a rapidly growing recognition of the extent to which progress in medical knowledge and its command of technical resources were becoming dependent on researches in a widening range of contributory sciences. Less than a century ago, even within the lifetime of some who are still living, the whole of the experimental background of medical science was still comprehended in the conception of "physiology," which had then, of course, not become clearly separated from anatomy. To-day, if you survey the whole range of the natural sciences—chemistry, physics, even some chapters in the applications of mathematics, and the group embracing all the different fields of functional and systematic biology, apart from those normally figuring in a medical curriculum, you will find it practically impossible to trace any clear or continuous boundary of demarcation, between what is already of obvious significance to the progress of essentially medical knowledge, and what appears still to lie beyond the possibility of such a connexion. It would be difficult indeed, as yet, to predict any medical interest for the investigation by astronomers of the extragalactic nebulae, or for the exploration of the higher reaches of pure mathematics by those whose minds can operate in that intellectual stratosphere. He would be a rash speculator, however, who would to-day exclude anything, in the whole range of natural knowledge, from the ultimate possibility of some medical application. Nobody, for example, is likely to have thought, but a few years ago, of the bending of the path of an electron in a magnetic field, or the disintegration of the atom of a heavy element under neutron bombardment into radio-active isotopes of other elements, as phenomena likely to have a special importance for the advancement of medical knowledge by research.

Yet, when the physical problems concerned with the design of the electron-microscope had been solved, and new orders of critical resolution and effective magnification had thus been brought within reach, it was soon evident that a large part of the interest in this new physical weapon was becoming centred upon its applications to problems of essentially medical significance, such as the nature of ultramicroscopic infective agents, viruses and bacteriophages, or the dimensions and shape of bacterial flagella. And when the advance of nuclear physics in another direction had taken a leap forward during the war, in this case behind a thick curtain of military secrecy, and the artificially contrived liberation of atomic energy by nuclear fission had thus become an accomplished fact, apart from further concern with destructive possibilities, and perhaps by an instinctive recoil from them, attention seems to have become first centred on the use of the full range of new radio-active isotopes, which had incidently become accessible, for medical researches into problems of metabolism and for new methods of therapeutic radiation. We might even suppose that the conscience of the human race, or of those sections of it which can fairly be credited with so uncomfortable an attribute, had found an offset to the horrors of Hiroshima and Nagasaki, in even a speculative prospect of doing something for neoplastic diseases, in particular.

Only a few decades ago organic chemistry, having been led far from its original objective into explorations of the limitless possibilities of artificial synthesis, had come to look with disparagement on the efforts of the newly self-conscious biochemistry. Biochemistry had come into being to deal with the formidably complicated chemistry of life and its products, which organic chemistry had, for a time, almost deserted. "Tierchemie ist Schmierchemie," was a catchword of those days; animal chemistry, they thought, dealt with smeary, indefinite messes, and was too repulsively difficult for a real chemist to expose himself and his reputation to the risks of contamination from its contact. To-day the pendulum of opinion has swung far back indeed, and we now find some of the world's leaders in organic chemistry eagerly grasping the opportunities offered by the chemical problems of life and its products. It was not merely, then, the emergency of war which so readily induced the leading organic chemists of the English-speaking world to combine in a study of the structural constitution of Fleming's penicillin, when Florey, Chain and their colleagues had demonstrated its transcendent medical interest and its chemical accessibility. You have heard, no doubt, that this study soon revealed the existence of several penicillins, differing from one another in minor points of constitution, and even led to the confirmation of this latter, in one case, by synthesis. Before that stage was reached, however, it had been necessary further to invoke the aid of a specialized physical technique, X-ray crystallographic analysis, as a guide to the final choice between alternative structures, which the chemical data would fit equally well. And, to complete that side of the picture, we should note that the interpretation of the spot-pattern of the X-ray spectrograms, to reveal the spatial arrangement of the atoms in the molecule, would involve the application of a method of mathematical analysis discovered by Fourier in 1822. This was regarded then, and for long afterwards, as an intellectual achievement having an austere beauty of its own, as a kind of mathematical poem, but as remotely unlikely ever to find any sort of practical application. In physics as well as in chemistry, indeed, we can observe an eagerness to-day in many who are working at points of rapid progress, to apply their knowledge and technique to biological problems and thus to make contact with matters of more direct concern to medicine. Many other examples spring to mind, far too numerous for mention; but I must not leave an impression that physics and chemistry are alone important, among the extramedical sciences, for the advancement of medical knowledge.

Let me, therefore, mention only one other example, illustrating the unexpected medical value of what had seemed an almost freakishly specialized hobby in systematic zoology. A contemporary of mine at Cambridge, the Hon. N. Charles Rothschild, father of the present Lord Rothschild, had come up from school with the reputation of having been for years addicted to the collection and differential description of all the different species of fleas which could be found, in the fur or feathers of every kind of mammal or bird which he could contrive to examine. As you may imagine, we, his fellow-students, were disposed to regard this hobby as rather less practically useful than that of collecting stamps, and as lacking even the stimulus, which the latter would afford, of competition with rival collectors. And then, many years later, the Commission sent to investigate the bubonic plague in India came to the conclusion that a flea was the probable vector of the plague bacillus to man, and a rat the probable reservoir. It thus became urgently necessary to know the distinguishing characters of all the fleas infesting the animals with which human communities were in habitual contact; and the knowledge, to obtain which months or years of research might have been needed, was then found to be all ready to hand, and waiting to be used, in Mr. Rothschild's collection and records.

I hope that, by citing these examples, I am not giving you the impression that I regard medical research as something so indefinite in its scope and so uncertain in its objective that it may be held to include practically any kind of research, in the whole range of the natural sciences. On the contrary, I think that the aim of medical research can be defined with unusual precision. Medical research is, surely, the investigation of the conditions of human health; of the causes and effects of its disturbance by disease or injury; and of the procedures conducive to its restoration. What I have been trying to make clear is that, apart from the direct approach to these problems by observation and experiment on the human subject himself, there is bound to be an ever-deepening extension of the quest for medical knowledge into territories with which other departments of science are primarily concerned. It is, further, of interest to recall how many of the independent sciences to-day —not only physiology and human anatomy, but botany, zoology and chemistry—took origin by budding or cleavage from the parent stock of medicine. The sciences as we know them now may remind us, indeed, of organisms which, when they have been multiplied and differentiated by many successive divisions and sub-divisions, find regeneration and renewal of vigour in conjugation.

There is a feeling abroad, indeed, in circles much wider even than those directly concerned with science, that medical research is an activity worthy of special encouragement. And a substantial expression of such encouragement has been forth-coming, from private generosity in many countries; in Britain in particular it has also been available, now for some thirty-five years, from an annual grant of public money administered by the Medical Research Council. No man to-day who feels a genuine impulse to make medical research an aim in life, if he can give evidence of the requisite ability, training and character, ought to have serious difficulty, then, in finding the support required to enable him to put his aptitude for it to the test of a practical trial.

"Medical Research as an Aim in Life" is to be my subject, then, this evening; but before I say anything further about it, I ought, perhaps, to make it clear that I am not concerned only with medical research as an exclusive occupation for the whole of a man's working career, or as the sole service to the community for which he expects to receive a livelihood. We should remember that nobody, until times which still seem recent to some of us, expected to be paid at all in this country for doing medical research; it seemed to be regarded as a form of mild indulgence, for the leisure of a man who earned his living otherwise, as by teaching, or practice—almost as a kind of addiction, to which he yielded if he could not help it. And, from one point of view, such a presumption might have a certain advantage, in making it at least likely that the few who did engage in medical research with any sort of persistence, would be men having a natural gift for it, and an urgent desire to do it for its own sake. On the other hand, there was always the possibility that we and the world might be missing some mute, inglorious Harvey or Lister, for lack of the opportunity to try the wings of his genius. I myself, through accident of opportunity, and contrary to all expectation, happen to have spent practically the whole of my working life in medical research. I have no feeling but gratitude for the exceptional privilege; but it has not led me to doubt that we shall always have to look, for the major contribution to the advancement of medical knowledge, to the men who are carrying a primary responsibility for teaching, or for the clinical care of patients. There is this radical difference, however, between the present position and that which persisted till thirty or forty years ago, that research, whether in the medical or other fields, is now recognized as a part of a man's service to the community, for which he may reasonably expect some remuneration; so that, if he is holding only a minor academic or clinical appointment, and has a large part of his time still free for research, he may expect by undertaking it to earn a significant supplement to his stipend. And the young man who has ideas which he is eager to exploit, or a problem at the solution of which he has a strong desire to try his hand, need not now feel that he is compromising his future, if he decides to test his powers as a research worker for a few years. Even if the result should not encourage him, or if circumstances should otherwise not allow him then to include research in a more permanent plan for his life's work, the time spent in gaining that experience will not have been lost. He will have had a direct and living contact with the methods of research, with its standards of evidence, its traps for the unwary enthusiast, its excitements and its frustrations; and this first-hand experience of what research means will have given him, as nothing else could, a critical insight into the merits of claims made for new discoveries or advances, and will strengthen and vitalize all his work for the application of medical knowledge, whether in teaching, administration, or practice. In a real though limited sense, medical research may continue for him to be an aim in life, even though he may never again take a direct and active part in it.

On many grounds, therefore, and over a wide range of possibilities, as a whole-time or, more commonly, a part-time commitment, for an experimental period or for the whole of a working career, I do commend medical research, as an aim in life, to any of you whose natural instincts and aptitudes lead you in that direction. And, since research is the only activity in the field of medicine on which I can speak with any background of experience, I am going to ask your attention to some random reflections on medical research—on the objects with which it has been undertaken, the methods by which it has been successfully pursued, and the ways in which an investigator may find and choose his problems.

(1) *What is the Object of Medical Research?* The answer might seem to be fairly straightforward; but it is tied up with a wider discussion of the purpose of scientific research in general, which is agitating some circles to-day. You have probably heard debate of the question, whether the true object of any kind of research is to discover scientific truth for its own sake, in complete aloofness from any immediate concern for its practical application, or, on the other hand, to discover the means of improving the material conditions of human life. The effects of attitudes which appear so radically opposed, as thus stated, need not be so widely different in practice. For those who claim that the object of research should be to increase knowledge for its own beauty and excellence are usually ready, not only to admit, but even to claim, with the support of striking examples, that the widest and most important practical developments have, in fact, originated from the kind of independent and untrammelled pursuit of scientific truth which they advocate; while those who insist that the material enrichment of human life is the only true function of science—it is one of the doctrines of the so-called dialectical materialism, as most of you probably know—are willing, and even eager, to recognize the free advancement of even the most abstruse kinds of knowledge as a means to that material end, and therefore to honour and encourage it. There would not, on those lines, seem to be much difference, other than one of emphasis, between the practical effects of the two attitudes. And, for my own part, I regard it as a matter of small concern, which of them a man may adopt as an ultimate theory or creed, provided that he does not attempt to give it too literal or rigid a practical application in the immediate problem of the planning or conduct of research. I have known a distinguished colleague in medical research to be subject to tiresome inhibitions, because he had persuaded himself that there must be something unworthy or inferior about a research with any obviously practical objective. The danger is much more likely, however, to occur in the opposite direction. Benefit to human life, as an ultimate aim of medical research, is so obvious as to be almost a matter of definition; as a lure to benevolence, however, or as a guide to public policy in support of research, it

has its too obvious dangers. A donor finds it difficult to refrain from specifying the problem on which his gift is to be used, and his choice is likely to be determined by sympathetic emotion; so that we may easily find, in some countries, funds subscribed for the attack on specified diseases in excess of those which can be usefully applied; and it must be obvious that the political credit which might accrue to one whose name was associated with the promotion of a successful attack on the problem, say, of rheumatism, must offer serious temptation to a Minister of the Crown.

We must be careful, then, not to confuse the theoretical or ultimate objective of research with the immediate policy of its planning. In medical research, as I said, the benefit of human health as the objective is almost a matter of definition or nomenclature; I myself could not attach any other meaning to the word "medical." But in the immediate planning of his own activities by a worker in medical research, or in the planning which cannot but affect the allotment of funds available for its promotion, it is peculiarly necessary not to allow a sense of the ultimate objective to intrude in the guise of facile sentiment and popular appeal. We must beware lest it produce a tendency to favour long shots, short cuts, premature claims and even disreputable "stunts," and a corresponding tendency to discount and to disparage the patient and resolute pursuit of new knowledge, by a mind unclouded by any urgency for practical achievement and alert to follow any unexpected clue if it seems to promise a discovery of new significance, even in a direction remote from the lines of the original research. As a guide to policy which, in relation to our own researches, may not always be a matter of easy and confident decision, it may be helpful to glance at the practice of some of those who have been responsible for some of the greatest advances in medical knowledge and, in due course, in medical practice.

William Harvey, it seems to me, approached his problems and used his opportunities of observation and experiment with just the instinct and habit of the inspired naturalist. "Nature herself," wrote Harvey, "is to be addressed; the paths she shows us are to be boldly trodden; for thus, and whilst we consult our proper senses . . . shall we penetrate at length into the heart of her mystery." And it was by such bold treading of the paths which nature showed him that Harvey was led to the first great medical discovery, by which he laid the foundation not only for a new physiology, but for all medical science. More than two centuries later Louis Pasteur, a mineralogist and crystallographer, having discovered the mirror asymmetry of the crystals of the two tartaric acids and the preferential digestion of one of them by a mould, followed, with the alert vision of genius, the clue thus presented, and was led by it to further discoveries, which laid the first course in the foundation of the new science of bacteriology. Lister, it may be thought, took the clue, presented by Pasteur's work on the putrefaction of dead tissues, and applied it directly to the problem of suppuration in the living body. But Lister did not begin there; for many years he had been studying and describing, with the patient attention of a naturalist, the clotting of blood and the circulation through the capillary blood-vessels, and its changes with inflammation. Lister's experience as a free experimenter and observer, and the habit of mind which it had engendered, made him ready then to seize and to apply the analogy which Pasteur's work presented. And I have sometimes even thought that, if Lister could have withstood a little longer the irresistible appeal of human suffering, and could have given a few months to an independent, experimental study of the sources and the modes of access to wounds of the bacteria of suppuration, before he so directly applied his discoveries and assumptions, surgery might have been able to short-circuit the episode of the carbolic spray and, perhaps, to arrive much earlier at the modern routine of asepsis.

Paul Ehrlich's campaign of Chemotherapy has led, under his own guidance while he lived and later at the hands of those who have followed, to revolutionary changes in the prospect of sufferers from a whole range of diseases due to infections; and this might well be cited as an instance of a scheme of medical research producing just the kind of practical benefits for mankind at which it was deliberately aimed, by the man of genius who planned it. Even the re-examination of the therapeutic potentialities of penicillin, with the success which all the world knows, probably owed much of its stimulus to the earlier success of chemotherapy with artificial remedies. Banting and Best's discovery of insulin, again, could be cited as a striking example of medical research driving straight to the practical objective with which it was undertaken. In all these cases, however, we must not lose sight of the extent to which the ground had been prepared and the problem posed by antecedent researches, which had no such practical outcome in the relief of disease, but without which the experiments which eventually produced the remedial discoveries could not even have been devised.

Altogether, I think that we ought to retain a consciousness of the ultimate philanthropic purpose of medical research; but that our recognition of it ought to put us on our guard, lest we allow it to lure us into attempting short cuts, shelving exceptions, discounting difficulties, or making premature claims, in the hope that we may be able to reach some dramatically practical result, without submitting to the full and exacting discipline of science.

(2) And that leads me to say a few words more about the general conditions under which medical research, like any other kind of genuine research, is carried out. It is so easy to get the impression, from the popular acclaim which greets its real or imagined achievements, that the life of the research worker must be passed at a level of emotional tension rather like that of a gambler. In past years I have had more than one young man come asking for an opportunity to do whole-time research, and to be paid for doing it, with little to show in the way of credentials, beyond a dislike for the idea of teaching or practice, and a feeling that research must, by comparison, be full of excitement and fun. I did my best to correct that impression. The research worker, if he is successful, may indeed have his moments of discovery and seemingly sudden revelation, from which he may experience more than a momentary exhilaration; but, in spite of what popular report may suggest, such moments do not come merely by fortunate accident. As has more than once been said, these sudden revelations, or seemingly accidental discoveries, come to the man who has earned them. More often than not they will have been earned by months or years of what may well have seemed an almost hopeless drudgery; by courage to face, without flinching or evasion, what T. H. Huxley called the tragedy of science—the shattering bereavement of seeing a beautiful hypothesis slain by an ugly fact; by an integrity which never shirks exacting standards of accuracy, or of critical control; and by humble acceptance of the answer which nature gives, when the questioner expected to get quite a different one and even tried, perhaps, unconsciously to extract it. Research may have its

abundant rewards, but they are earned by submission to a stern discipline. And I think that it is a discipline from which a man would gain and keep something for a subsequent career in any kind of medical practice, administration, or teaching.

(3) Then, with regard to the finding and choice of subjects for research, let me say that I think that a not too exacting demand of duty in ward or clinical department, in laboratory, lecture-room or administrative district, bringing the holder regularly into living contact with the problems of health and disease, may even give him a definite advantage over one whose whole duty, for every day and all the time, is to do research and present its results. The difficulty, of course, is that duties and routine activities, which should provide a seed-bed of ideas and problems, and keep the worker's feet on the ground by preventing his attention from losing sight altogether of the ultimate significance of medical discoveries, are all too apt to become an embarrassing distraction, or a stifling incubus. How often a man must think that, if he could only get free from these insistent demands of daily obligation and be given the opportunity to concentrate his mind on research, he could push quickly ahead, towards the solution of an urgent problem which he has encountered. And, in many cases, there may well be substance in such regrets and aspirations. But there is another side to the picture. From my own experience, and some knowledge of the experience of others who held appointment with me in a Research Institute, with no formal duty but to do research, to be fruitful in ideas and to multiply discoveries, I can testify that such a privilege brings with it its own psychological strains and difficulties. There is the teasing uncertainty, whether the condition or phenomenon, on which one has decided to centre his attention and his effort, has really such significance as one had supposed; the suspicion, when the research is not quickly fruitful of result, that one will be left with nothing to show for months or years of striving and worrying; and the haunting fear that the fountain of ideas, which seemed to flow so freshly, will dry up as youth and middle age give way to the years of decline, leaving him with no reserve of teaching or practice, by which he could have earned his bread and served his fellow men. I can testify that, under such conditions, many a man, who has eagerly embraced the freedom and seemingly unhampered opportunity of whole-time research, has looked with envy at the

position of a colleague, who has no reason to fear that he is not justifying his existence and his stipend, if his research should hang fire for a time.

I have no reason to feel anything but gratitude for the opportunity which I have enjoyed; but the general position is very different to-day from that with which I began. There were then but scanty indications that medical research, in the intervening forty-five years or so, would so astonishingly and so radically change the whole aspect of preventive and curative medicine. There were no Beit Fellowships till some years later, and the Government's Medical Research Fund was still a decade or so ahead. So, when I was offered a research appointment supported by industry, I accepted, and held it for ten years; and I had no reason to regret the experience, from which I passed directly to the service of the Medical Research Council. And I am glad to think that there are men to-day who are doing work of high quality for medical science and finding problems in abundance ready to hand, in research departments supported by industry.

Looking at the possibilities now emerging, however, with the results of research at last making their full impact on practically every phase of medical activity, I think that, if I myself were starting again, I should probably be looking for the opportunity to do research in conjunction with some academic, clinical or laboratory appointment, in hospital or, perhaps, in public health service, and to find in one of these the problems for research. There is one particular kind of service to which, as it seems to me, the medical research talent of this country has not yet done its full duty, or made full use of its opportunity. I have in mind the medical service concerned with the health of our tropical colonies. The past record of British medical research activity in the tropics is one of which we have good reason to be proud; the names of Manson, Ross, Bruce, Leishman and others belong to a great history. Here, in any case, should be still an attractive prospect for the man with a pioneering instinct and a spirit of adventure, to work in a field where many nuggets of new discovery are likely still to lie near to, or even on the surface, waiting for an alert vision trained in research to recognize them. And to-day, I expect that recruits with the right kind of ability, and some spirit of adventure, if that still exists, would find the training at their disposal on attractive terms, and would not have to fight for it, to find it or make it for themselves, as the old stalwarts did.

We need not go so far afield, however, or even into a whole-time service, to find opportunity presenting itself to the man with the true research instinct. James Mackenzie did the best of his epoch-making researches on heart disease and its treatment in time spared from a busy general practice in Lancashire. Dr. William Norman Pickles, of Aysgarth, is to-day using the special oppor-tunities of a general practice limited to the villages scattered along Wensleydale, for the scientific collection and analysis of data concerning the spread of epidemics of the common infectious fevers—data such as could not otherwise be obtained. If a man has the true impulse to do medical research, he will find the opportunity for it under conditions in which we have not yet learned to expect it.

We shall probably not all hold exactly the same opinion about the future of medical practice, and the effects on its value to the community of the new conditions which the National Health Act imposes. I think that we can all agree, however, that no pressure of form-filling, certificate-writing and report-making which a centralized administration may involve, must be allowed to weaken the personal, professional and scientific standards of the practitioner. Research has been providing, and will continue to provide, a new basis of scientific knowledge for increasingly certain diagnosis and for ever more directly effective treatment. Reorganization of the basis of practice will have no value, unless it enables these results of research to be made more readily available to the patients whom they can help. We ought all of us, as a profession, to insist on the right to keep that flag flying, to let it be known that we have no use for changes which do not help us to regard medical research more clearly as an aim, to keep pace more easily with its progress, and to apply its discoveries more quickly and effectively, for the benefit of anybody who needs them.

WILLIAM WHITLA AND QUEEN'S UNIVERSITY, BELFAST*

LET ME first give expression to my very deep sense of the honour you have done me, in making me a Doctor of Laws of this great University, now in the hundredth year of its activity for higher education and research in Northern Ireland. You may be assured that I value very highly indeed the distinction which you have thus conferred.

You have honoured me further by asking me, as my first act as honorary graduate, to perform a simple but significant ceremony. It is my privilege now to declare this fine Assembly Hall open, and to offer it for acceptance by the University, of which you have given me the right proudly to call myself a graduate member.

As all present will know, the building and equipment of this Hall have been made possible by one of the generous provisions made under the Will of the late Sir William Whitla, one of this University's most widely distinguished sons, and one of its greatest and most consistent benefactors. This building will most fittingly bear his name, so that all the members of the University, who enjoy its provision for their corporate activities, will be regularly reminded of one who, throughout the whole of a full life and an active career, gave to the advancement of the University's interests, in all directions, a central place in his thoughts and his endeavours. He had a more complete and life-long association than is usual in an academic career, or in his own chosen profession of a physician, with this one School and University. Here he entered as a student in 1871, graduated M.D. in 1877, and became Professor of Materia Medica and Pharmacology in 1890, retiring from the chair in 1920, but giving the University still his full service as its Parliamentary Representative at Westminster; here he remained till he died, full of years and honours, in 1933; and, in addition to his provision for the Hall, which we are here to dedicate to the uses which he designed, he bequeathed his residuary

---

* An Address delivered at the opening of the Sir William Whitla Assembly Hall, Queen's University, Belfast, Saturday, 19th February, 1949.

estate to the University, and his own beautiful house and garden in Lennoxvale as a lodge of residence for its Vice-Chancellors.

I myself had only once the opportunity to meet Sir William Whitla, at the meeting of the British Medical Association here in 1909, when he was its President. I think that, even from that friendly and encouraging, though brief, encounter, I must have received some impression of what he was and what he had accomplished; but it has been deepened into an almost incredulous admiration by all that I have since learned of him and his career. For it seems to me that any one of his several major activities would be to-day thought enough, by itself, to fill the working life of a man, even of exceptional powers. The duties of teaching and research, which belong to a Chair of a subject so wide in scope as Materia Medica and Pharmacology; the writing of several important and highly successful text-books for students and practitioners of medicine, and the keeping of these abreast of the advances of knowledge by frequent revision; or, again, the diligent service of the sick, and clinical teaching therewith, in the Royal Victoria and other Belfast hospitals, and the successful conduct of a very large practice as one of Northern Ireland's great consulting physicians; any one of these, I feel, might now be regarded as constituting, by itself, a full contribution by one man to the activities of a university and to the life of a community, and as leaving him no more than a necessary margin of leisure. Yet the records leave no room for doubt that William Whitla, at the height of his powers and his reputation, carried them all with ease, taking them in his masterful stride.

And it is certainly not possible to suspect him of a merely perfunctory pluralism. His lectures won a high reputation, and we are told that they were enlightened by characteristic flashes of genuine eloquence—an achievement indeed, if one considers what openings for rhetoric would be offered to an ordinary exponent by the Materia Medica; while the resounding success of his text-books carried them far across the world, calling for no less than twelve successive editions of one and for translations of another into nearly all the languages of civilization, including Chinese. And these ever-growing claims never made him a slave to his professional and academic duties, or narrowed the range of his interests. He kept throughout life a close connexion with and a generous interest in the Methodist community in which he had been born and reared.* And, with this evangelical faith of his fathers, he kept a habit of Bible study, finding, as Isaac Newton had done in his day, a special interest in the prophetic chapters of the Book of Daniel; he published indeed, a full translation, from their original Latin, of Newton's almost-forgotten writings on the subject, with his own introduction and commentary. His colleagues and friends have remembered him, by way of contrast, as an incomparable raconteur; they have recalled his general grasp of English literature as "amazing," and his knowledge of the works of Shakespeare, in particular, as quite remarkable. Each year, when the late Sir Frank Benson and his Shakespeare company visited Belfast, William Whitla used to entertain them at well-remembered supper-parties with his friends. Yet he still found time to travel; and his colleagues remember the vivid accounts which he gave of his experiences in Russia, Palestine, Italy, and other parts of the world.

We are left with the impression of a generous amplitude of culture and achievement, for which it would be difficult, I think, to find parallels to-day. William Whitla was undoubtedly a man of unusual and individual distinction; but his career belongs in many of its aspects to the tradition of the great Victorian era, though his life extended, in fact, through the reign of Edward VII, and most of that of George V. He was born in 1851, a year rendered almost symbolic by the first Great International Exhibition, in London; and in 1890, when he was elected to his Chair and entered upon the main phase of his academic and professional career, Victorian standards of success and Victorian ideals of conduct and culture had, in general, not yet encountered any strong challenge. We can find then, I think, a special fitness in his lifelong association with a University which, founded as a constituent college of a wider "Queen's University" for Ireland, when Victoria and her reign were still young, to-day, with its independent University status, still commemorates the great Queen in its title.

Those who, like myself, belong to the generation which followed his, will not, I think, even now condemn the impulse

---

* After I had made this statement, my attention was drawn to an item in the Commemorative Exhibition showing that, on his form of entry to the University, William Whitla had described himself as "Presbyterian." It must be presumed that he joined later the Methodist community, possibly on his marriage.

which, in England at least, led us who were still young in the "nineties" to seek to break out of the Victorian tradition into what seemed to us a freer air. It is the eternal right and privilege of youth thus to challenge the credentials of its parents' beliefs, standards, and conventions. But we ought to be ready to confess that we may have shown too great an eagerness to discard a core of ripened wisdom, together with a rind of what seemed to us a smug convention. In the homely figure of an old-fashioned German saying, we were too ready, in our haste, to throw the baby away with the bath-water. It may be that the world is even now paying a penalty for this excess of our eagerness, as well as for all the mistakes of the generations which have followed ours.

There is truth in the suggestion, I think, that, just as the great civilizations of ancient times had a substratum of slavery, our parents of the Victorian era had shown a blind spot, or at least a too easy tolerance, for gross contrasts between the luxury of mounting wealth and the squalor of grinding poverty. But they did believe in individual ability, industry, and courage; and I think that we should credit them with having set themselves with determination to give increasing scope to these, wherever they could be found, and steadily to eliminate such inequalities as were due only to historical accident and social inertia. They were busily building more and wider educational ladders, but they were to be ladders—not lifts or escalators. I think that they still regarded mere jealousy as the meanest of human motives, and would not have allowed it ever to masquerade as a virtue. While they so readily imposed upon themselves, as individuals, embargoes and restrictions which their descendants may have found tiresome, or even ludicrous, they cherished, and advocated with passionate conviction, an ideal of individual freedom for all mankind—an ideal which, in spite of all the tragic sacrifice made so recently in its defence, has been roughly blown upon from different quarters in these latter years by partisans of political dogmas, which, in spite of their shouts of enmity to one another, have shown a remarkable concurrence of contempt for individual freedom. And, with all their timid reluctance to recognize some of the discoveries of their own greatest men, our Victorian predecessors had firmly accepted, and were ready fiercely to defend, the most sacred of all rights to a university—the right of a man's mind to seek the truth and to proclaim what it finds, in complete freedom from any pressure of politics, prejudice, or preconception.

You will agree, I think, that the great problem for a university to-day is to provide for the students who, in such rapidly swelling numbers, already throng its precincts, an education which will open to them this full freedom of the book of knowledge, and encourage in them the spirit of free enquiry; and which, at the same time, will give them an anchorage in essential truths and tested principles, enable them to use that freedom wisely, arm them against the plausibilities of propaganda, and fit them to play their due part in to-day's tremendous task of shaping world opinion and determining world policy.

And where shall the basis of such an education be found? Where shall we seek this true humanism to-day? The times are long behind us when one mind could expect to comprehend, or even to make useful contact with the whole extent of human knowledge and achievement. Even within that rapidly widening range which comprises the natural sciences, the mere segment even, of one of its main divisions, of which any one man can hope to maintain an expert knowledge and intimate understanding, becomes smaller year by year. If William Whitla could return to-day, he would find that his own subject of medicinal treatment had swung already into a new orbit of achievement, in which it can now deal directly with the causes of disease and not merely, as in the so recent times of his own full activity, with the relief of its symptoms. How shall a university prepare its students to play their proper part of trained and intelligent leadership and active contribution by research, in a civilization so dominated by physical science, for immeasurable good, or, if man's folly so determine, for irreparable disaster? And how shall it give them, at the same time, an enlightened understanding of all the great past, as well as of the present and the potential future, of man's creative activities in literature, philosophy, and all the liberal arts?

There would, I expect, be no approach to unanimity among us on a solution of the problem. Many still hold, I believe, with fervour and sincerity, that a study of the history of man, and of what human hands and brains have made, must always, and for all of us, provide the basis of a finer educational discipline, and open the door to a wider culture, than any which the study of nature's works can offer. I myself am frankly doubtful of the claim of such a belief to stand on firmer ground than that of tradition. Some of William Whitla's teachers here, in days when the building of scientific foundations for medicine had hardly yet begun, were, indeed, ripe classical scholars before they became learned physicians by long experience; but William Whitla himself, starting from school with a few years' apprenticeship in pharmacy, and trained only in medical subjects in his later student years, achieved a culture, it would seem, as liberal as any of theirs. And, when I hear claims for the incomparable breadth of a culture based on classical scholarship, even in this scientific age, I find myself puzzled by the contrast between scientific colleagues, with their shamefast reluctance to let gaps appear in their literary or artistic equipment, and eminent scholars among my friends, who still seem to find in their ignorance of modern science a matter even for pride—of modern science which, even though we resent it, will inevitably contribute in increasing measure, not only to the material framework of our daily life, but to the very texture of our thoughts.

Each of us, I do not doubt, will find that his own answer to this educational conundrum differs, at least in detail, from that of all the others. For my own part, I pin my faith to the power of a university to give to the student of any subject in its curriculum, if rightly presented, a feeling for precision in knowledge and thoroughness in its mastery, for the adventure of exploration beyond the boundaries of the known, for victory over intellectual difficulties, and for the passionate pursuit of truth as something to be supremely valued for its own sake, not to be misused as a mere expedient, or as a crutch for some dogma. I believe that either the data of science, or those of literary or historical scholarship, can be made intellectually deadening if they are indifferently presented; but that either can be made the means of awakening the mind to the joy of knowledge and of intellectual triumph, and of creating therewith a fertile soil in which sound judgment can grow with the ripening years.

Believing then, in depth, even though circumscribed, rather than shallow breadth, as the proper aim of a direct and deliberate culture, I am the more convinced of the need, in this scientific age, to maintain in any university an adequate balance between studies of all the different aspects of man's intellectual activities and adventures. True width of culture cannot be given in these days by any attempt to make students what Isaac Newton would have called "little smatterers" over the whole range of science and scholarship. But I believe that it can and will come, in a university, from the free converse and daily association of those who teach and those who learn in all its faculties, however special and restricted the formal studies of any group may perforce become, as the sum of tested knowledge mounts and accumulates.

It is just those opportunities of multilateral contact and exchange that a university can offer, as a principal factor of its educational opportunity. Looking back over the years to my own experience as a student of natural science in a university, I believe that the daily encounters and nightly talks with fellow students reading the classics, history, or moral philosophy, were as important a factor in my education, at least in my earlier college years, as any formal tuition in my own subject. And this splendid Hall, now opened for the use of all the members of this University, will stand as a permanent symbol, and offer continuous opportunity, for those corporate and social activities on which the character of university education so intimately depends; and, in doing so, it will perpetually commemorate to the University that famous man among her sons, Sir William Whitla, whose generous filial piety bequeathed it to the University in which so much of his life was passed, and on which so much of his thoughts and his affections was centred.

THOMAS ADDISON: PIONEER
OF ENDOCRINOLOGY*

THOMAS ADDISON was second in that matchless succession of physicians and morbid anatomists—Richard Bright, Thomas Addison, William Gull, and Samuel Wilks—whose work at Guy's Hospital in the earlier and middle years of the nineteenth century raised to such heights the reputation of this school as a great centre of medical teaching and investigation, and contributed so much to the foundation of the great nineteenth-century tradition of advancing medical knowledge by the accurate study and differentiation of diseases in the clinic, closely linked with an equally thorough scrutiny of their results as seen after death. The names of two of them, Bright and Addison, have been permanently associated with diseases which they thus described; the number would be three if we included the name of Thomas Hodgkin, who was curator of the museum here in the same period, though never on the clinical staff. Two of them again, Addison and Gull, can be regarded as clinical pioneers of endocrinology. In Gull's case we ought to associate his achievement with that of another and younger Guy's physician, Hilton Fagge, whose recognition of absence of the thyroid as the cause of cretinism enabled Gull in 1874, in describing "a cretinoid condition in adult women" now known as myxoedema, to associate it with atrophy and functional defect of that gland. That, however, was a quarter of a century later than Addison's first mention of a condition which he had discovered, now known everywhere as Addison's disease, and which he then described as "a remarkable form of anaemia" regularly associated with disease of the suprarenal capsules.

TWO PIONEER COMMUNICATIONS

The late Sir William Hale-White,† whose long life enabled him to transmit to more than one later generation the great tradition

* The Addison Lecture given at Guy's Hospital on 23rd June, 1949.

† *Great Doctors of the Nineteenth Century*. Sir W. Hale-White. Arnold and Co. 1935. To those who wish to learn more of Addison's life, personality, and

of this school from a time when Addison was still held in living memory here, has suggested that "the whole of endocrinology dates from March 15, 1849"—this being the date on which Addison made the first, short communication on his disease to the South London Medical Society. I believe that a good case could be made for that claim. There had, indeed, been earlier accounts of diseases—diabetes mellitus and exophthalmic goitre—which were shown much later to have a causal relationship to endocrine disorders. Even cortical tumours of the suprarenals had been recorded early in the nineteenth century, and hirsutism noted in a girl patient; but again without clear recognition of an aetiological relationship. I think, therefore, that we may agree with Sir William Hale-White that endocrinology began effectively with Addison's paper, which in 1849 made the first clear attribution of a general morbid condition to defect of a ductless gland; and you will note that the date gives a centenary character to our celebration of this great man and his achievement.

Addison's fuller account of the disease which now bears his name was published six years later, in 1855, as a separate slender quarto with fewer than 46 pages of large printed text, richly illustrated with coloured lithographic plates and bearing the title *On the Constitutional and Local Effects of Diseases of the Suprarenal Capsules*. You will note that even the title emphasizes the aetiological inference. On these two pioneer communications by Addison the author of a recent textbook on the now enormous science of endocrinology makes apt comment: " . . . They show how much can be accomplished, without any of the modern clinical and laboratory facilities, by keen observation of the living and dead patient. They are prominent examples of concise and descriptive medical writing." They are so indeed; no better model could be recommended to the many who to-day seek to give permanent record to observations which are, in the main, of slighter significance.

A remarkable feature of the publication of 1855 is that, by way of introduction to the principal theme, Addison describes and differentiates another new disease, for which, by contrast,

---

achievements, the chapter on him in that volume is recommended. It gives references to other accounts of him by Samuel Wilks, who was his pupil, and Lonsdale, a lifelong medical friend.

he had failed to discover an adequate cause by examination post mortem. This he named "idiopathic anaemia," but it is now generally known as "pernicious" or "Addison's" anaemia. It is not clear that he had at first distinguished with certainty between these two fatal diseases, in both of which anaemia and lassitude were prominent; but there is no doubt about the distinction in the book of 1855. His object there was to give an exact account, based on a series of cases, of what he called "bronzed skin" or "melasma suprarenale," known to us as "Addison's disease." The description of "idiopathic anaemia" is given only by way of introduction, to explain that the author was looking for additional cases of this condition when, in his own phrase, he "stumbled upon" another major discovery, which is the main subject of the book.

So that this slender volume contains the first full description of two new diseases; and, to quote Sir William Hale-White again, "Addison's account of each is so perfect that nothing has been found wrong in his clinical picture, and nothing has been added except facts that have been obtained by instruments which he did not possess, and a few occasional symptoms not present in the cases which he describes." I think it should be added that, if Addison had looked at the marrow in the long bones of the patients dying of pernicious anaemia, his acute eye could hardly have missed its unusual appearance. Even without any of the technical equipment which has made haematology a later possibility, he might in this case also have associated what he could see post mortem with the general disease. He certainly could not have foreseen, however, that the bone-marrow defect and the consequent anaemia would be traced many years later, in 1926, to the failure of a kind of endocrine control normally exercised by the liver; and even remoter from any conception possible to Addison, or to anybody till very recent years, is the news from two different research centres, in America and this country, of the isolation this year of the immensely active agent responsible for this endocrine control of the haematopoietic function, and the remarkable discovery that cobalt is an important element of its composition. Perhaps we may regard that, too, as an achievement suitably commemorating the fact that pernicious anaemia, which this potent hormone (or vitamin) so dramatically relieves, was first recognized by Addison about 100 years ago.

OTHER ACHIEVEMENTS

When Addison's book describing the diseases was published in 1855 he was already 60 years of age. It would be very remarkable if he had first begun to make and to publish discoveries of such outstanding merit so late in life. In fact, he had already made and published others in an impressive series; and some of these, in particular those dealing with pneumonia and phthisis, were regarded by his pupil Wilks as the highest of all his achievements. What is really remarkable is that they should have been so little recognized and so widely forgotten. His earliest publication of importance was a characteristically perfect description of the clinical appearance which he found to be associated with, and diagnostic of, a fatty liver. Then in 1839, when he was 44 years old, in a book, *Elements of the Practice of Medicine*, which he published with his senior, Richard Bright, Addison gave the first descriptions of appendicitis and its consequences—"descriptions," according to a modern writer, "so clear and well presented that they could not be surpassed to-day." Later he gave the first correct account of the pathological process of lobar pneumonia; he published observations calling for a profound modification of the earlier conception, due to Laennec, of the destructive process in pulmonary phthisis; and he discovered and described xanthoma, which he called "vitiligoidea." And all these contributions to the advancement of medical knowledge, any one of which might be judged adequate by itself to have given him high rank as an investigator, were made by Addison before he discovered the two diseases which bear his name, and thereby keep it in general remembrance among those who study and practise medicine.

When Addison came to London after graduation in Edinburgh, he gave his time and interest for some years chiefly to diseases of the skin. This interest he retained after he had begun his career at Guy's, where he entered as a student in 1817; it was he who later superintended the making of the beautiful wax models of skin conditions which are still one of the great treasures of the pathological museum here. He seems to have been rather a proud and shy man, not easy of approach; but none of the Guy's men in that great succession stood higher in reputation with his colleagues and pupils as a physician or as a teacher.

Much of his time was spent, and practically the whole of his professional interest was centred, in this hospital. Outside it he sought no recognition, and he received but little. Only late in his career was he elected to the Fellowship of the Royal College of Physicians, and he held neither lectureship nor office there. He was never even proposed for the Fellowship of the Royal Society, and he was never a physician to the Court. Here you will keep him in proud memory as the greatest of all, perhaps, of the great medical investigators and teachers who were members of the staff of this hospital in that period. As his pupil, Samuel Wilks, wrote of him: "For many years he was the leading light of Guy's, so that every Guy's man during the thirty or forty years of his teaching was a disciple of Addison, holding his name in the greatest reverence, and regarding his authority as the best guide in the practice of his profession."

THE DEVELOPMENT OF ENDOCRINOLOGY

In the medical circles of a wider world Addison will be remembered chiefly as a pioneer of the science of endocrinology —as the man who first entered and opened to other explorers a new territory which in the intervening century has been extended in all directions and brought under a most vigorous cultivation. There have been periods in which doubts of its further fertility have become prevalent and have seemed even to be natural, but it is to-day yielding harvests of medical knowledge in overwhelming abundance and in bewildering variety. I am going to invite you now to follow me in a preliminary survey, at the best a most cursory review, of the lines of development along which the present position has been reached. Then I shall endeavour to speak in somewhat greater detail of the course of the advance, including some recent and intricate phases, of knowledge of the endocrine functions of the particular ductless glands, the suprarenals, which, through Addison's discovery, provided endocrinology with the point of its very beginning, and which are now providing a focus for some of its most recent and most rapidly progressive developments.

I think we may assume that, brilliant and accurate observer as he was, Addison went as far as it would ever have been possible to proceed with the advancement of knowledge of an endocrine

defect by simple observation of the results of a natural process
at the bedside and in the post-mortem room. His work came
at the end of the purely observational period and at the beginning
of a new epoch, in which deliberate experiment was to play
a dominant part. It is curious, indeed, that the use of the experimental method in medicine should have fallen so long into
abeyance. William Harvey had shown what it could do, and
had particularly enjoined its use on his fellow physicians, two
centuries earlier; but before Addison's day English physicians
appear to have forgotten Harvey's injunction, and to have
left the use of experiment to surgeons like John Hunter and
Charles Bell. And when a major revival of the experimental
method came, opening the era in which we are still living, it
began, not in Harvey's England, but on the European continent.

There, in Paris, the founder of modern physiology, Claude
Bernard, in his experimental studies of the glycogenic function
of the liver had reached and propounded the general idea of
an internal secretion into the blood. The idea was not an entirely
new one; its germ can be found in medical writings at least
as early as 1775; but Bernard gave it form and an experimental
basis. He was not directly concerned, however, with the
specifically acting internal secretions of the glands with which
endocrinology normally deals; and, apart from what had been
known since prehistoric times of the effects of castration, the
first attempt to study the function of an endocrine organ by
deliberate experiment must apparently be credited to Brown-
Séquard, who began to remove suprarenal glands from animals
by operation in 1856, the year after Addison's book was published.
His animals all died rapidly; but any significance which his
results might otherwise have claimed seems to be called in question
by his frequent record of fatality following unilateral adrenalectomy—an operation which later workers, using a clean surgical
technique, have uniformly found harmless. In any case, neither
he nor Tizzoni (1886), nor Abelous and Langlois (1891), who thus
later confirmed the fatal effect of double adrenalectomy, contributed much more than a confirmation of Addison's conclusion,
from his study of Nature's experiments, that the function of the
suprarenals was for some reason a vital necessity.

It was in 1856, again, that Moritz Schiff reported that extirpation of the thyroid gland was fatal to dogs—many years, it will

be realized, before the clinical studies of Fagge and Gull brought to light the connexion between defect of thyroid function and cretinism or myxoedema. There can be no doubt, however, that the effect which Schiff thus early observed was mainly due to his removal of the parathyroid glands with the thyroid, to which in the dog they are closely attached. This was eventually made clear by the work of Gley in 1891; but, before this, Schiff had himself shown that successful grafting of a portion of a dog's thyroid gland, which presumably contained a parathyroid, would protect it from the normally fatal result of removing the remainder. And after Gley's demonstration of the separate function of the parathyroid glands the possibility and protective effect of grafting these alone was shown by von Eiselsberg (1892), Leischner (1909), and others.

Meanwhile the experience of Reverdin and of Kocher on the myxoedematous or cachexial condition following surgical removal of the human thyroid for goitre, and Horsley's production in 1884 of an artificial myxoedema by thyroidectomy in the monkey, had brought the experimental work on the thyroid again into closer relation with the observed results of its atrophy in man. And then in 1891 came the first successful application of these experimental findings in practical therapeutics, when Murray, of Newcastle, showed that myxoedema could be successfully treated by administering an extract of sheep's thyroid—a notable milestone, indeed, on the road of advance in endocrinology. In this case, at least, the formation of an internal secretion was no longer a matter of inference; it had become a demonstrated fact

This advance was followed, however, by a long and discouraging delay, which was especially obvious on the side of remedial application. When I myself, as a student first began to be conscious of physiology and its progress, Horsley's experimental results and Murray's triumphant application of them were still relative novelties, and there was great interest in the likelihood of analogous therapeutic success in diseases due to defects of other ductless glands. As the years went by, however, such possibilities seemed to become increasingly remote. Plenty of observers were trying to correct such defects, whether resulting from disease or from experimental removal, by administering glands in substance or as artificial extracts; but no convincing

success was for many years obtained in such other cases—neither
with the parathyroid and suprarenal glands, nor with the gonads,
nor with the pancreas, the removal of the latter having been
found by Minkowski, in 1889, to cause a diabetes mellitus. With
all these glands, on the other hand, protection against the effects
of removal was obtainable by the establishment of successful
grafts in advance.

It began to be believed, and the conviction grew and hardened
with time, that the thyroid might be unique among these pre-
sumptively endocrine organs in the stability of its active principle,
or in the extent to which this was stored in the gland so as to be
available at a given moment for extraction. It had not, indeed,
been established even yet, by strict evidence, that these other
organs had in fact an endocrine function: one or another of them,
if not all, might conceivably act by destroying an injurious by-
product rather than by supplying a factor necessary for normal
metabolism. And while this position of doubt remained, the
progress of endocrinology, especially on the side of remedial
replacement, was of necessity halted. Thus there grew, for a
time, a discouraging tendency to suspect that the experimental
method, like that of clinical observation before it, might be
approaching the limits of what it could achieve in this difficult
field of inquiry. Then, after some thirty years, came the discovery of insulin by Banting and Best in 1921, revolutionizing
the treatment of pancreatic diabetes, bringing a whole range of
metabolic problems within the scope of new and progressive
exploration, restoring to work on the ductless glands the earlier
spirit of hopeful enterprise, and sounding the advance into a new
phase, in which endocrinology is still expanding with a speed
which now puts a strain on the alertness and the scientific equipment of anyone who endeavours to keep pace with its headlong
progress and its dazzling changes.

There have, of course, been a number of other important
factors of this astonishing acceleration. One has been the concentration of studies on the pituitary body, in the medical and
surgical clinics as well as in the experimental laboratory, and
especially on the control over the functions of other ductless
glands which is exercised by the hormones of its anterior lobe—a
control which led the late Sir Walter Langdon-Brown, and
others who have adopted his picturesuqe phrase, to describe the

pituitary anterior lobe as "the conductor of the whole endocrine orchestra." Another has been the rapid elucidation of the once baffling interplay of endocrine activities involved in the sexual cycle. Yet another and most important factor has been the discovery of the true plan of the chemical structure of the sterols and their derivatives, providing the key to the chemical nature and relationships of the whole series of steroid hormones, including, as we shall see, those of the suprarenal cortex as well as those of the gonads.

We must make no further attempt, however, to range over the whole endocrine landscape. Any one section of it, if an endeavour were made to deal with it in full detail, could now provide the material for a whole course of lectures by somebody equipped so to present it. For several reasons I must bring our inquiry now to a narrower focus, and in the rest of this memorial lecture I shall ask you to look with me, still in rather hasty survey, and without any pretence at more than an occasional reference or attribution, at some of the recent developments of knowledge concerning the subject of Addison's own pioneer investigation, the suprarenal glands.

THE SUPRARENAL MEDULLA

We must recall first that it was not till 1895 that it began to be understood that the suprarenal body consisted of two functionally different glandular organs bound together as cortex and medulla. In that year Oliver and Schäfer discovered the remarkable immediate actions of simple extracts from the gland when these were injected intravenously or, as in later experiments by others, were applied locally. Then the active principle responsible for these intense immediate effects was found to be localized entirely in the medulla of the gland; and just after the end of the nineteenth century it was isolated, as adrenaline or epinephrine, and eventually made by synthesis.

Meanwhile it had been discovered by Lewandowsky and by Langley, and then further demonstrated in fullest detail by Elliott, to whom the pure adrenaline was available, that there was a remarkable and unquestionably significant correspondence between the actions of adrenaline and those of the true sympathetic nerves. It is well known how Elliott's penetrating early suggestion (1904) that sympathetic-nerve impulses transmit their effects by liberating small charges of adrenaline at the endings of the nerve fibres was verified many years later by Loewi's brilliantly simple and convincing experiments from 1921 onwards. It thus became a component of a now familiar and wider scheme which pictures the effects of all efferent peripheral nerve impulses as evoked by the liberation of one or another chemical transmitter at the nerve endings. There remained, however, some grounds for uncertainty whether the adrenergic transmitter was always, or entirely, "adrenaline" itself, though the correspondence was so close that nobody doubted that there was a definite chemical relationship. The late W. B. Cannon took care to leave the question open by referring to the transmitter always as "sympathin"; and, apart from a further hypothesis which led him to complicate this terminology, Cannon was clearly right in emphasizing the departures from complete identity between the actions, on the one hand, of artificially applied adrenaline and those, on the other hand, of sympathetic-nerve impulses and of the actual transmitter escaping from the site of its liberation into the blood stream and carried therewith to act on a distant organ. I myself, as early as 1910, had emphasized the tendency of adrenaline to exaggerate the inhibitor in relation to the augmentor components, as seen in the corresponding actions of sympathetic nerves. In comment on Elliott's hypothesis, I had even then pointed out that the primary amine corresponding to adrenaline (*nor*-adrenaline, then known commercially as "arterrenol") reproduced the actions of sympathetic impulses with an even closer fidelity, in this respect, than adrenaline itself.

The evidence did not then seem to warrant a direct suggestion that *nor*-adrenaline might be the transmitting agent, or even a component thereof. Elliott's suggestion had at that time received but little notice, and *nor*-adrenaline was known then, and indeed till quite recently, only as a product of artificial synthesis.

But now, in the past year, the evidence has begun to flow in, arising simultaneously and independently in a number of different laboratories and in several different countries. Differential physiological reactions, contrived with much ingenuity and reinforced by fluorometric measurements, have made it possible to determine the proportional contributions of adrenaline and *nor*-adrenaline to the sympathomimetic activity of a fluid containing both.

And by such methods it has been possible to prove that the sympathetic transmitter, as extracted from the sympathetic chain or from a purely adrenergic nerve, or found leaving the spleen in its venous blood during stimulation of its adrenergic nerve-supply, consists mainly of *nor*-adrenaline, with adrenaline itself as, at most, a minor component. Even the hormone secreted

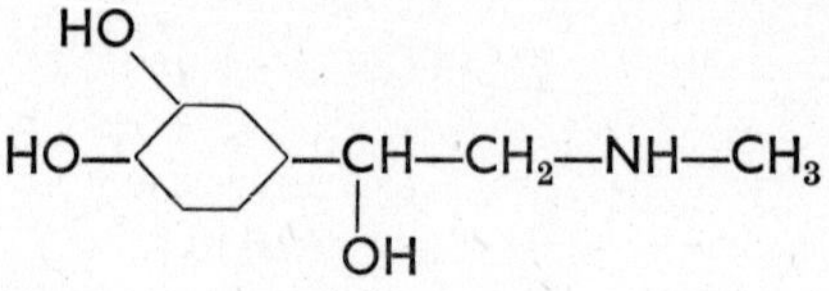

$$HO-C_6H_3(OH)-CH(OH)-CH_2-NH-CH_3$$

ADRENALINE

$$HO-C_6H_3(OH)-CH(OH)-CH_2-NH_2$$

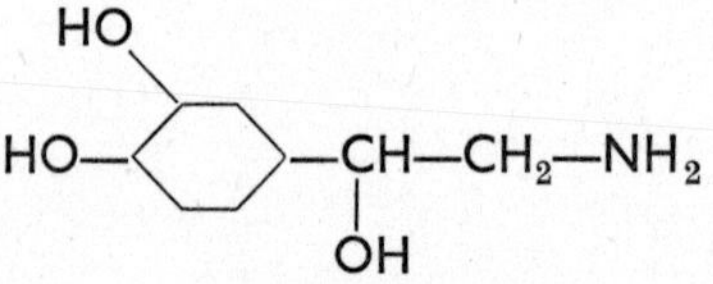

NOR-ADRENALINE

Fig. 1.

into the blood from the suprarenal medulla when the splanchnic nerve is stimulated, though it usually consists mostly of adrenaline during the early stages of such a stimulation, contains *nor*-adrenaline in increasing proportion as the process is repeated, and may, even after several periods, consist almost entirely of this primary amine.

These discoveries have interest for the pharmacologist and the chemist, and they remove certain puzzling discrepancies, but they make no fundamental difference to our conception of the endocrine function of the suprarenal medulla. We still regard it, following Cannon, as contributing immediate reinforcement to sympathetic-nerve actions on occasions of emergency, of sudden calls for activity, or of emotional stress; and its hormone still figures also as the peripheral transmitter of the effects of adrenergic impulses. Only our conception of its chemistry is slightly changed. When first the actions of this medullary hormone were discovered it was natural to expect that a lack of it would be found to play at least an important part in the symptoms of Addison's disease, and evidence for such an effect of its exclusion was eagerly sought. As a result, however, we are left without any clear reason for attributing any conspicuous item of the Addisonian syndrome to simple lack of the endocrine function of the medulla. It is remarkably difficult, in fact, to detect any significant result from the removal of one suprarenal gland and extirpation of the medulla from the other. Even when Cannon removed, in addition, the whole system of the true sympathetic ganglia from cats, the animals remained healthy and exhibited only an unusual placidity. The fact that a melanin pigment is formed by oxidation of adrenaline or of its primary homologue might well suggest a connexion between a medullary defect and the bronzed skin of Addison's disease. Even in that case, however, there is no direct experimental evidence. Extirpation of the medulla does not cause any comparable pigmentation, though the possibility still remains open that a disorder, rather than a suppression, of the medullary metabolism normally producing the adrenalines may be responsible for the appearance of Addison's pigment.

What is now abundantly clear is that the main features of Addison's disease—the increasing debility and languor, the muscular weakness, the low arterial pressure, the decrease in blood volume, the disturbance of the normal balance of inorganic salts between body fluids and tissues, the liability to attacks of hypoglycaemia, and the general lack of the normal resistance to infection, poisoning, temperature changes, or any kind of harmful influence, this complex of symptoms leading to the inevitably fatal termination of untreated Addison's disease—are due entirely to the lack of the hormones formed by the cortex. It becomes ever clearer, indeed, that when Addison described his "melasma suprarenale" he was dealing with the collapse of a main arch of the functional structure by which a large proportion of the functions and reactions concerned in the maintenance of a healthy vitality are kept under endocrine control and regulation, and that the keystone of that arch was to be found in the hormones of the suprarenal cortex.

CORTICAL HORMONES

After long discouragement and frustration, as an important item of the new and accelerating advance which set in after insulin was discovered, Swingle and Pfiffner in 1931 succeeded at length in preparing a stable and approximately purified extract of the cortical hormones by systematic injection of which life could be maintained in an animal deprived of its suprarenal glands. It was not long before, from several laboratories in different countries, crystalline fractions began to be obtained from cortical extracts, and a little later again the chemical nature of these began to be clarified. A few years earlier the chemical identification of pure hormones from the suprarenal cortex would have seemed an almost fantastic aspiration. Its achievement was greatly facilitated by the recognition, then recent, of the widely varied physiological significance of substances built by the attachment of different substituent groups and side-chains to a common hydrocarbon skeleton—the so-called cyclo-penteno-phenanthrene nucleus, forming the central structural feature of the sterols, the bile-acids, certain remedial glucosides, the steroid vitamin D, the steroid sex hormones, and, now, the steroid hormones of the suprarenal cortex. Many investigators have contributed to the amazingly rapid advance of knowledge of these substances, and mention can be made only of work by Kendall, and his co-workers of the research laboratories of the Mayo Clinic, in isolating several of these hormones from animal suprarenals, and of that of Reichstein, and his co-workers of Basle University, in producing members of the series artificially by synthesis.

At least six such active cortical steroids are known in pure crystalline form, and there is a highly active amorphous residue, probably containing a number of others. The evidence available concerning the different activities of those already isolated would by itself provide material for a course of lectures by an expert. In broadest terms, the hormones already recognized fall into certain main groups. The members of one such group are oxygenated at the carbon atom numbered 11 on the structural formula, while those of another group differ from the former only in having no oxygen in this position. Corticosterone (Fig. 2, I) is a representative member of the former group, the actions of which are particularly concerned with carbohydrate metabolism. When given in excess they cause breakdown of cellular proteins, rise of blood sugar amounting to a temporary diabetes, with resistance to insulin, greatly increased excretion of uric acid, and a steep decline in the number of eosinophil leucocytes in the circulating blood. As a group, they may be regarded as the carbohydrate-controlling cortical hormones. A type of the other group is desoxycorticosterone (Fig. 2, II), and the characteristic

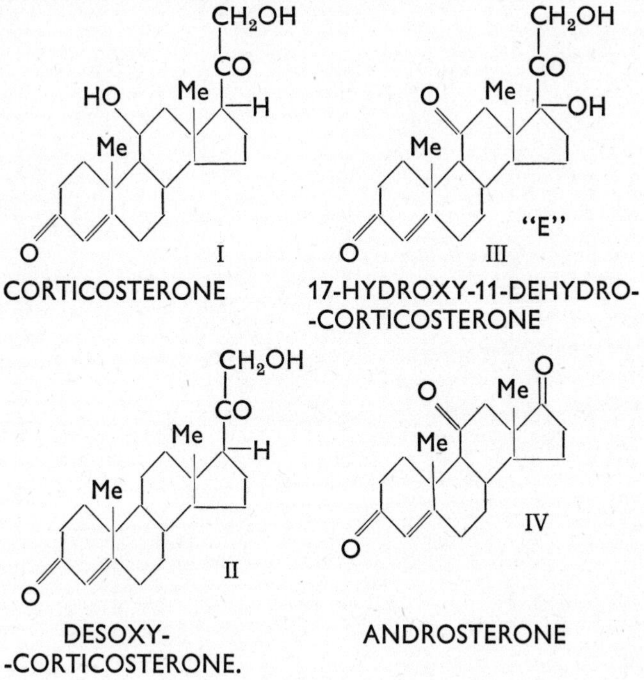

CORTICOSTERONE

17-HYDROXY-11-DEHYDRO-
-CORTICOSTERONE

DESOXY-
-CORTICOSTERONE.

ANDROSTERONE

Fig. 2.

action of these is to maintain the balance of inorganic salts in the body, with preponderance of sodium and chloride in the fluids and of potassium and phosphates in the cells. Lack of these hormones, which may be referred to as the salt-controlling group, causes loss through the urine of sodium and chlorides from the blood and body fluids and appearance in these of excess of potassium; administration of these hormones in excess causes over-retention of sodium and chlorides and water-logging of the tissues. Both these types of endocrine control are deficient in Addison's disease, and both must be replaced to preserve life, though lack of salt-controlling hormones can to some extent, and for a time, be made good by an added intake of sodium chloride. And there is another group, derivable from the 11-oxygenated series by replacement of the side-chain on the 17-carbon atom by oxygen; and the members of this group, of which androsterone is a type (Fig. 2, IV), closely related to testosterone, the hormone of the testis, have indeed a sex-hormonal virilizing action.

CONCLUSION

The outlines are beginning to appear of the most complicated pattern of the complementary actions of these hormones in relation to one another; of their balanced actions against those of other hormones—for example, of some of them against the actions of insulin; and of the control of their formation and output by the so-called adrenocorticotropic hormone of the pituitary anterior lobe and apparently to some extent by the suprarenal medullary hormone adrenaline. I myself observed, as early as 1921, that a cat from which the suprarenals had been removed showed a greatly exaggerated sensitiveness to histamine, even before overt general signs of deprivation appeared. And, in more general terms, the part played by the cortical hormones in the whole scheme of the endocrine control of the body's functions and reactions, and especially, as Selye, of Montreal, has emphasized, in its adaptative reactions to almost all kinds of injury or stress, is undoubtedly one of central importance.

In further and most suggestive illustration of this function, in the case of at least one of the corticosteroids comes the recent news of therapeutic trials, at the Mayo Clinic and elsewhere, giving promise of a protective and curative effect of another member of the carbohydrate-controlling group, the 17-hydroxy-11-dehydrocorticosterone (Kendall's "Substance E," Fig. 2, III)*, against defective or perverted adaptative reactions responsible for rheumatoid arthritis. We shall wait eagerly for further evidence of advance in this new and surprising direction. And meanwhile I think you will agree that, if the anterior pituitary lobe occupies the conductor's rostrum in the endocrine orchestra, we must at least assign the leading violinist's desk to the suprarenal cortex. And surely no artificial monument to the memory of Thomas Addison could be so imposing as this great and now so rapidly growing tree of health-giving and life-saving knowledge, sprung from the seed which Addison dropped as he worked in this hospital with such patient devotion and with a clinical vision unsurpassed in its clarity and alertness.

---

* Now, of course, generally known as "Cortisone."

SOME PERSONAL MEMORIES
OF LORD RUTHERFORD*

I HOPE I shall be able to communicate to my listeners some part of the emotional satisfaction that I experience in being able to speak of my own memories of Ernest Rutherford, one of the world's great men in his own generation, in centres so intimately associated with his birth and early childhood, and with his education in school and university. During the tour which the New Zealand Government's invitation and hospitality have enabled me to make, I have seen the schools at Foxhill and Havelock in driving through those places, though the buildings are probably different from those of Rutherford's childhood; the headmaster of Nelson College has been kind enough to spend some afternoon hours in showing me the school as it is, with the Rutherford relics which it preserves, though, there again, the present building is not even the first replacement of the wooden structure where Rutherford studied. At Canterbury University College, Christchurch, I have been privileged to see the small cellar, the "den" as the commemorative brass plate describes it, where his first experimental research on "wireless waves" was begun; and I have seen there also the site, now in different occupation, where formerly stood the old laboratory for physics and chemistry, locally remembered as the "tin shed" and now to be seen only in photograph, where that first research was brought to the point at which Rutherford transferred it overseas from Christchurch to Cambridge.

I was never linked to Rutherford, as many were, by the close bonds of direct collaboration and shared interests in scientific research. I can claim, however, to have known him well, and to have been honoured by his friendship, as long as anyone now living who met him first after he left New Zealand; for I knew him from the time of his arrival at Cambridge as a post-graduate research student in 1895, till he died all too early in 1937, as a

---

* A lecture delivered in April, 1950, to the Cawthron Institute and the Nelson Philosophical Society, Nelson, N.Z.; and at Canterbury University College, Christchurch, N.Z.

world-famous professor in that university. We met as fellow-students, post-graduate and undergraduate, of the same College, and as members of the same Natural Science Club, both at Cambridge; and some thirty years later we became closely associated for five years as fellow officers of the Royal Society of London.

Ernest Rutherford was born in 1871 at Spring Grove, near Brightwater, thirteen miles out of Nelson. A photograph of the little wooden cottage has been preserved, and is reproduced in the late Professor Eve's biography of Rutherford; but the house itself has disappeared. There appears to be some local rivalry, indeed, of claims to have been the place of Rutherford's birth, between Spring Grove and Brightwater as they are to-day. The most likely account of the matter suggests that the Rutherford home, though belonging to Spring Grove as defined when he was born there, was later incorporated into Brightwater township, so that each of the still contiguous territories has some basis of claim.

Ernest was one of eleven Rutherford children. His father, James Rutherford, son of an early settler, seems to have been primarily a wheelwright by trade, but to have combined this with small farming. With one of several brothers settled in the same neighbourhood, James Rutherford seems also to have been engaged in logging and making sleepers for the railway then being built, and in flax-milling when the railway construction was suspended. These varieties of occupation, together, presumably, with the claims of a rapidly growing family for accommodation, entailed several removals, with consequent changes of school for the children.

It is proper that the world should remember Ernest Rutherford as a son of New Zealand, and of its South Island in particular; for though his discoveries belong to mankind, and though the opportunities to make them came to him almost entirely in other parts of the British Empire, the conditions of his childhood, youth, and early manhood here must have had a strong influence on the development of his great natural endowments. He would surely, indeed, have shown greatness of ability and character in some direction, if he had been born in Dundee, from which his father's father, or in Hornchurch in Essex, from which his mother's mother came to New Zealand, both as relatively early immigrants and settlers. It was after the early death in Hornchurch of her husband, who is rumoured to have been a man of remarkable ability, that the maternal grandmother had come to New Zealand with her young daughter; and some have been disposed to trace a major share of Ernest Rutherford's inheritance of ability to this English grandfather whom he never knew. However that may be, I think that we may safely assume that the same fortunate combination of parental genes must anywhere have produced the essential Rutherford. But the conditions of the new country into which he was born, in which he spent his childhood, and to which his thoughts always went back as his home—the daily contacts with individual craftsmanship and husbandry, the constant demands for contrivance, opportunism, and independent enterprise, the freedom of the open country and the bracing encounters with physical hardship, danger, and even tragedy, as when it fell to him to take the news to his mother that two of his younger brothers had been drowned in a boating accident in the Pelorus Sound—all these must surely have added strong fibres to the texture of the boy Rutherford's experience, and favoured the sound and firm ripening of his great natural gifts of ability and character.

To these steady influences exercised by his parents and home surroundings, there was to be added, from quite early years, the more formal stimulus of excellent schooling. Ernest Rutherford's father would have inherited a traditional Scottish faith in the value of education, and his mother had herself been a school teacher before her marriage. "I should never have been where I am to-day if it hadn't been for my mother and father," said Rutherford in after years, referring to the personal sacrifices which he knew that his parents must have made, in order to ensure for him the education which his talents merited. From the first he was very fortunate, too, in his teachers. With other members of the family, it appears that he had his first childish schooling at Spring Grove, where his mother had taught before her marriage, in succession to her own mother. The father soon moved with his family, however, to Foxhill, some ten miles farther south, and it is at the primary school there that we can identify Ernest Rutherford's first able teacher in Mr. Henry Ladley, who had charge of his education between the ages of $5\frac{1}{2}$ and 11 years. The family then made a further move to Havelock, on Pelorus Sound, and at the school there young

Rutherford had such stimulating teaching from Mr. J. H. Reynolds that, four years later, at the age of 15, he won a scholarship to Nelson College, with an astonishing total of 580 out of a possible 600 marks in all his papers. At Nelson College again he was fortunate in the two headmasters of his time, Mr. Ford and Dr. Littlejohn, who seem to have transmitted respectively much that was best in English and Scottish scholastic traditions. Dr. Littlejohn's system was centred on the classics but extended to a wide range of other disciplines, and especially to a sound training in mathematics. Mr. C. H. Broad, who was Ernest Rutherford's contemporary at Nelson College, and who himself later succeeded to the headmastership, tells me that chemistry came to Rutherford as a new subject when he entered the sixth form, and required hard work from him to overtake the others. By 1888, however, when he was over seventeen, he was top of the sixth form in all subjects, and was reported by the master to show special promise in mathematics.

We learn from one of his schoolfellows that Rutherford used later to say that, if he had not won the scholarship to Nelson he would probably have been a farmer. It is tempting, indeed, to speculate as to what might then have happened. The bearer of the greatest name in natural science at a much earlier stage of its development in Britain, Isaac Newton, did actually leave the school at Grantham, in Lincolnshire, when he was sixteen, in order to take charge of the family farm for his widowed mother. Newton, however, was so often a truant from his farming to indulge his passion for mathematics, that his mother most fortunately sent him back to school, and thence in due course to Trinity College, Cambridge—whither, more than two centuries later, Ernest Rutherford was to follow him. Rutherford seems to have shared with Newton a schoolboy faculty for making mechanical models. On the other hand, he never showed any of that aloofness and self-absorption, which were to make Newton an almost morbid recluse during so large a part of his Cambridge period. As a boy, Rutherford showed, indeed, no kind of freakish precocity; he had a robust and normal enjoyment of life, of play as well as work, and he excelled in studies over so wide a range that, even at the end of his period at Nelson, his interests had not yet found a particular focus. If chance, then, as he himself thought possible, had earlier made Rutherford a farmer, I believe he would have been a very good one. There was a beginning, when he was young, of a very progressive application of science to agriculture, and this might well have fired his imagination. In one direction or another, we may be sure that Rutherford could have done good service to farming and agricultural science in New Zealand; but even New Zealand, I think, was better served, in the long run, by the career into which the further course of his education led him. For it gave, not merely scope, but wings to his soaring genius, and made him a benefactor of mankind at large, as leader of that tremendous advance in the physical sciences which, in the course of a few decades, was to transform for all of us the very way in which we think of the ultimate nature of the material universe.

After his all-round successes at Nelson College it was natural for Ernest Rutherford to win a Junior Scholarship to the University of New Zealand; with this he matriculated in 1889, to enter Canterbury College, Christchurch, at the normal age of 18. By 1892, when he was 21, he had graduated B.A. and had won a Senior University Scholarship in mathematics, which at that stage was still regarded as his strongest line. After another year of mathematics under Professor Cook and, in addition, of chemistry and physics under Professor Bickerton, Rutherford graduated M.A. with the unusual distinction of double first-class honours, both in mathematics and physical science. And then came a crucial fifth year, in which he continued to work at Canterbury College, for a higher research degree in natural science. Then it was that he began his first experimental researches, working, it would appear, largely on his own initiative, and feeling the first thrill of success as an original discoverer.

These first experiments at Canterbury are noteworthy, indeed, not only for the bright promise which they gave of Rutherford's later supremacy among experimenters, but also as providing, in essence, the methods and ideas for his first research at Cambridge, which was, in fact, an extension of them. When he thus began to try his hand at research at Canterbury College, the experimental demonstration by Hertz, of the possibility of producing the invisible, electromagnetic waves which Maxwell had foreseen in theory, and which we now call "wireless waves," was still an exciting novelty. Young Rutherford set up a Hertz oscillator in a cellar at

Canterbury College, which he was allowed to use for the purpose, actuating the instrument with an induction coil, or with an electrical machine of a type then in use. A brass tablet in the outside wall of this "den" now marks the place of this historic event. He found that the alternating current impulses, which he thus generated and transmitted as waves across the room to a receiver, if they were made to pass through a little coil of fine wire, would magnetize steel needles or iron wires inserted into the coil, or change the strength of their magnetization if they were magnets already; and thus the little coil with its core was made to change its position, if it had been suspended in a magnetic field. He investigated this phenomenon very completely, and later published a description of his findings, which had involved him in the measurement of time intervals as short as the 100,000th part of a second—a really remarkable technical achievement for a beginner, in those pre-electronic days. He seems to have recognized early the practical possibilities of his little bundle of magnetized needles, with its surrounding coil of insulated wire, as a detector of the Hertzian waves, and to have made with it a contrivance which enabled him, while still at Canterbury College, to record a wireless signal transmitted the whole length of the physical laboratory, the lower storey of the "tin shed" of those days, and through several intervening walls—about sixty feet in all; and since he achieved this in 1894 or 1895, he must, at that point, have been some years in advance of the similar observations by Marconi, which were to have such tremendous practical developments.

Rutherford at 23, however, had reached no premature climax of ability, or of mental enterprise, such as Isaac Newton seems to have attained at that age. To a fellow student at Canterbury College he seemed to be just "a boyish, frank, simple, and very likeable youth, with no precocious genius; but," his friend continued, "when once he saw his goal he went straight for the central point"; and that early personal estimate also contains something prophetic of the man he was to become.

Probably the most important effect of this first research work at Canterbury College was that it opened for Rutherford the possibility of going to Cambridge, to work there under J. J. Thomson. The Commissioners administering a fund which had been derived from the profits of the first great International

Exhibition, held in London in 1851, had created Overseas Scholarships, to enable young science graduates from Dominion universities to continue their researches and make wider contacts, in British universities and other appropriate centres. The candidates were to be put forward by their own universities, and 1895 was the year of New Zealand's opportunity. Rutherford was one of the two presented by the University of New Zealand, and, after an initial uncertainty, he became its first Overseas Scholar. He borrowed the money to pay his passage to England, and set out in September, 1885, for London and Cambridge. Many years later, when he had become the world's acknowledged leader in the new physics, and was President of the Royal Society of London, Rutherford himself became one of the Commissioners administering the 1851 Exhibition Fund. Some alternative claim on the income had led members of the Board to raise the question whether the Overseas Scholarships were still serving their purpose. This roused Rutherford to a characteristic intervention, as free from anything like mock-modesty as it was from any hint of pretentiousness. "You might remember," said he, "that if there hadn't been any Overseas Scholarships you wouldn't have had any Rutherford here!" And the Overseas Scholarships are still being awarded.

Rutherford had arrived in Cambridge in 1895, as one of the first batch of post-graduate research students admitted there from other universities; and, on J. J. Thomson's recommendation, he entered himself as a student of Trinity College at the beginning of the October term of that year. "He wished me to join Trinity," he wrote home at the time, "which is his own college and also the best as well as the dearest in the university." One can imagine that this question of cost, to one dependent upon the slender support of the Scholarship, may well have been a matter of more immediate concern, even than the imposing traditions of a College where Isaac Newton, Clerk Maxwell, and Lord Rayleigh had been students and fellows before him, as well as "J.J." himself. I was then an under-graduate scholar of Trinity, beginning my second year. The new post-graduate research students, of whom the College had accepted a number, dined in the Hall at the bachelors' table, so that I did not begin to meet Rutherford regularly there till nearly two years later. We ordinary Cambridge students, like not a few of our seniors, were inclined at first to look a little askance at these representatives of a new species, older than ourselves by several years, and neither just under-graduates, nor proper dons, as we might have said. We soon found, however, that most of them fitted into the picture remark-ably well. Rutherford was probably the most brilliant of them all, though we might not have recognized him as such for ourselves. He was open and friendly in his manner, simple and direct in his judgment of matters on which he thought himself entitled to an opinion; but he was free from any trace of those airs of portentous wisdom, of effortless brilliance, or artificial enthusiasm, which a clever under-graduate from the English schools was often tempted to assume, and which his contemporaries were too ready to accept at their face value. If we had been inclined to look critically at Rutherford, I think that we young cynics might have described his manner as rather hearty, and even a little boisterous; but I can imagine us allowing, with pride in our tolerance, that a man who had been reared on a farm, somewhere on the outer fringes of the British Empire, might naturally be like that, and might nevertheless have the remarkable ability which rumour was beginning to attribute to him.

I had new opportunities of contact with Rutherford soon after 2nd May, 1896, when he was elected a member of the Cambridge University Natural Science Club—a small and intimate body of some twelve members, under-graduates and younger graduates who were supposed to have shown some special promise or line of interest in science. I became a member at the meeting after that at which Rutherford was elected. The meetings were held in the rooms of the members in rotation, on Saturday evenings; and the member thus entertaining the Club was expected to provide coffee and some light refreshment with it—sardines on toast formed the standard provision in those days—and then to read a paper, or make a communication, on some matter of current scientific interest, usually, of course, in the range of his own special studies or knowledge. Naturally the post-graduate research students who joined the Club were expected to have something special to say about their own work, since they had the advantage of being already engaged in researches, about which we juniors were only hearing or reading; and I have a very vivid memory of a meeting held in Rutherford's lodgings in Park Street—then a row of houses looking out over Jesus Common to the not distant River Cam. From his letters home to his mother, and to Mary Newton of Christchurch, who was to become his wife, it is clear that, on arriving at Cambridge in the autumn of 1895, he must have settled down to repeat and extend his Canterbury College experiments on the detection of the Hertzian waves at a distance. We know that he had brought his little electro-magnetic detector with him from New Zealand, and had taken the opportunity, made by a call of his ship at Adelaide, to demonstrate it to W. H. Bragg, who was then Professor of Physics there. He writes from Cambridge on December the 8th, 1895, that he "can get quite a large effect at twenty yards"; but from other evidence we know that he had already achieved that before he left Christchurch. On 21st February, 1896, however, there is a long description of an attempt to obtain transmission through about half a mile across the Common, which failed, because, as he discovered with relief, his detector had broken down at the critical moment. And then, on 29th February, he is able to record that, on the day after this failure, he had succeeded in detecting waves from the Cavendish Laboratory to Townsend's lodgings, more than half a mile away, and "through solid stone houses all the way." It was not till July of that year, however, that he began to tell the Natural Science Club about these experiments. Like other students 'in statu pupillari' he had at that date moved into College, as temporary occupant of an absent student's rooms, during the Long Vacation; and on 25th July Rutherford entertained the Club in the College rooms which he was thus occupying, and read a paper on "A New Method of Detecting Electric Oscillations." The Club minutes show that, as might be expected, what Rutherford described was "his method of detecting oscillations by means of the effect they produce on magnets," and that "the paper was illustrated by showing some apparatus used in his experiments." On this occasion, then, he only showed the Club his detector, without demonstrating its action. The next Club meeting for which Rutherford was responsible was on 15th May, 1897, and is recorded as held in his lodgings at 49 Park Street. The title given for the paper in the Club's record is "Invisible Radiation." There is no minute giving the gist of it, but I am sure it must have dealt with wireless waves to which the title would quite well have applied at that time. For this is the only meeting on record as held at Rutherford's rooms in Park

Street, and I remember very clearly his demonstrating there the possibility of detecting Hertzian waves originating in the Cavendish Laboratory, half a mile away.

As my memory pictures the scene, he had the receiving apparatus on the table of his living-room, and he had contrived that the effect of the waves on his electro-magnetic detector should somehow start the ringing of an electric bell. He explained to us that he had arranged with somebody in the Cavendish Laboratory to start the Hertz oscillator there at exactly 9 p.m. by the laboratory clock, by which he had carefully set his watch; and we all sat round the table waiting for the great moment, like a racing-boat's crew counting the seconds to the starting gun. Exactly at nine o'clock the bell began to ring, and we greeted the demonstration with cheers; and then Rutherford gave us a short talk on the nature of the transmission which we had been witnessing. I wonder whether any of us had any sort of premonition of what might be the future of this wireless communication at a distance, of which we had been given so early a demonstration. Many years afterwards, when we used to meet often at the Royal Society, I remember Rutherford recalling this early work on wireless waves, and pondering for a minute on the possibility that he might have continued in that line of interest, instead of being diverted from it by the remarkable new discoveries of X-rays and natural radio-activity. For the news of these came in the autumn of 1895 and in the immediately following years, and was soon exciting the interest of even a wider world than that of the physicists; and Rutherford was easily attracted thereby into researches of a more fundamental type, and with less easily marketable possibilities. He never showed, in fact, any interest in, or any instinct for, making money by inventions.

This meeting and demonstration in Rutherford's student rooms were remembered, when he and I were guests, more than thirty years later, at a dinner celebrating the completion by the Cambridge Natural Science Club of some number of hundreds of its meetings. He was then the President, and I was one of the Secretaries, of the Royal Society; and speaking after dinner in the vein appropriate to such an occasion, I recalled the meeting in Park Street, and made the scandalous suggestion that Rutherford probably had a bell-push under the carpet, to press with his foot when the bell was due to ring; to which he, in rollicking mood, replied: "I have little doubt that my friend Dale's unworthy suspicions were fully justified."

Almost up to the year of Rutherford's arrival at Cambridge, physics had appeared to be a body of admirably exact, but almost completed knowledge. Years later J. J. Thomson recalled "the pessimistic feeling, not uncommon at that time, that all the interesting things had been discovered, and all that was left was to alter a decimal or so in some physical constant." In 1894, the year before Rutherford left New Zealand, Lord Salisbury, addressing the British Association at Oxford, had reminded his hearers that, in spite of the attractive speculation that the atom of every element might be "only a greater or smaller number of hydrogen atoms compacted by some strange machinery into one . . . the reply of the laboratories has always been clear and certain, that there is not in the facts the faintest foundation for such a theory." And, further, that "what the atom of each element is, whether it is movement, or a thing, or a vortex, or a point having inertia . . . these questions remain surrounded by a darkness as profound as ever." When physics or chemistry, then, came down to fundamentals, while both could claim to be making some advance in precision of measurement and in refinement of their methods of observation, both seemed at that time to be laboriously approaching a limit, beyond which science could not hope ever to penetrate to any new certainty, either by observation or by theory. And then, all at once, a new and rapidly accelerating movement began, piercing this boundary wall of finality and advancing again into a still widening vista of new knowledge. And it may be counted as one of the significant coincidences of scientific history, that this new epoch in man's understanding of physical reality began only a month or two after Ernest Rutherford's arrival at Cambridge, when Röntgen discovered the X-rays. I well remember the news of that event reaching Cambridge, at first through reports in the daily papers, which emphasized, of course, the vision of opaque bones through transparent flesh. "What nonsense will they publish next?" said a lady at a Cambridge dinner party a few days later; and the chorus of frivolous incredulity was only hushed, when the well known and authoritative bark of J. J. Thomson, who was one of the guests, cut across it. "But why should it be nonsense?" said he. "It seems to me the kind of thing that is likely to be true." I remember a meeting of the Natural Science Club in the rooms of the late Sir Joseph Barcroft, on 29th February, 1896, at which a Crookes's tube, borrowed from the Cavendish Laboratory, was used to photograph the shadow of Barcroft's door-key through an ordinary, wooden dark slide. That was before Rutherford's election, and I do not remember his being present; I suppose that somebody must have taken me as a guest. And then, some years later, I remember that the Club met in the rooms of my Trinity contemporary, the Hon. R. J. Strutt, who was later to succeed his great father as Lord Rayleigh. Strutt entertained us with an account of the rays given off constantly by a salt of uranium, even if it was kept always in the dark, which M. Becquerel had detected by their action, like the X-rays, on a photographic plate. I remember the late Sir James Jeans, who must have been a guest for that meeting, protesting that, if this were true, it would involve an infraction of the law of the conservation of energy; and I remember Strutt's reply. The facts, said he, seemed to be beyond doubt; M. Becquerel was an observer of undoubted competence and integrity; and it was so much the worse for the law of the conservation of energy. This, remember, was many years before the conversion of matter into energy began to be a seriously considered possibility. This must, I think, have been after Rutherford left Cambridge for Montreal; for, if he had been present, I am sure that my memory would have retained some characteristically vigorous and penetrating comment by him. These discussions of the Röntgen rays and of the Becquerel radiations from uranium, by the Natural Science Club in Cambridge, seem, therefore, to have taken place, the one before and the other after the few years in which Rutherford was an ordinary member; and I mention them only to recall the wave of excitement which was sweeping over the world of science in those days, when the first breach had just been made, and was being so rapidly widened, through what had seemed to be the unpassable boundary of the classical, molar physics.

Even before he gave us the demonstration of wireless waves at long range, Rutherford had already begun to work with J. J. Thomson on the X-rays, and especially on the ionization of a gas which they produce as they pass through it. Rutherford had passed the air, containing the ions which the X-rays had produced, between parallel plates bearing positive and negative electric charges, and had shown that the ions were attracted to the oppositely charged plates and gave up their charges to them. "Ions are jolly little beggars; you can almost see them," he said long afterwards to Dr. Eve at Montreal. But while he was still at Cambridge, there are records showing that Rutherford had also begun to work already on the spontaneous radiation from uranium, that he had recognized two components in it of different penetrating powers, and that he had provisionally named these, even then, the alpha- and beta-rays; so that he had made a real beginning there of what was to be the great work of his life. As early as October, 1896, at the age of 25, he is writing from Cambridge to Mary Newton: "Don't be surprised if you see a cable some morning that yours truly has discovered half a dozen new elements, for such is the direction my work is taking." Little wonder that he was soon beginning to be known among physicists, in Cambridge and beyond it, as a young man of very uncommon potentialities. We find him in the same year giving a lecture-demonstration to the British Association, at its annual meeting in September, 1896. Remember, too, as further evidence of the rapid enlargement of the physical horizon then in progress, that 1897 was to witness J. J. Thomson's first announcement of a sub-atomic particle, the electron, in a lecture at the Royal Institution in London.

The last event to be mentioned in Rutherford's early period at Cambridge was one of some concern to me personally, namely, his election to the Coutts-Trotter Research Studentship at Trinity College, late in 1897. This was the only research emolument of its kind then available, to a Trinity student of science who had not yet become eligible for a College Fellowship, and the Trust Deed required its award for research in physics or physiology. To tell the truth, I had begun to keep my eye on it, with a view to a possible application in the following year, when I should have taken my final University examination. If Rutherford, then, were to hold the Studentship for the full two years, it was clear that it would not be available at the time when I had hoped to try my luck; and I remember feeling a little forlorn about it, and wondering whether we ordinary fourth-year students would ever have a chance again, in competition for such opportunities with this constellation of brilliant graduate seniors, which the fame of J. J. Thomson and Trinity was now assembling in the

College from all corners of the Empire. Nobody, however, could criticize the award to a man of Rutherford's outstanding distinction, or begrudge anything to one of his genial and straightforward character.

Rutherford resigned the Coutts-Trotter Studentship in the summer of 1898, so that, after all, it was vacant when I wanted it. The College faced, I suppose, with the difficulty of choice between a physicist and a physiologist, divided it between Strutt and myself, finding some other expedient to make up its value to both of us; and we were both very proud thus to divide between us the succession to Rutherford in this studentship. The reason for his resignation was his appointment, at the age of 27, to the Chair of Experimental Physics at the McGill University, Montreal, in succession to an already world-famous physicist and experimental engineer, Professor Callendar. It is recorded that when, later, Professor Bovey, of Montreal, remarked to J. J. Thomson that they all had been very sorry to lose Callendar from McGill, he was rather startled to receive the blunt reply: "I don't know why you should be; you got a better man anyway."

And there, for a longish period, I must interrupt my personal memories of Rutherford. He was at Montreal for nine years, from 1898 to 1907; and what wonderful years they were for him and for physical science! The wisdom of Rutherford's moving, at that juncture, to Montreal might to some have been a matter of doubt. For Cambridge had already become one of the world's chief centres of the new movement in physics, while in Montreal there might be relative isolation; and a young man, who had still to make himself known in the wider scientific circles of the world, might be expected to find it difficult to go forward on his own unsupported initiative. Any forecast of that kind, however, would have been very wide of the mark where Rutherford was concerned. So far from lacking confidence and initiative for independent research on this new order of phenomena, Rutherford within a year or two was making Montreal the centre to which the whole world was turning with an almost incredulous expectation; he was showing already a penetrating vision, an experimental resourcefulness and an intellectual courage, which soon made him the recognized leader into the new world of atomic and sub-atomic physics.

Everybody with closer interests in scientific happenings knew of Rutherford's work for nine years at Montreal, partly in conjunction with Soddy, in which so much was achieved towards revealing the nature of the intricate phenomena of atomic breakdown as the cause of natural radio-activity, and the bearing of these on the chemistry of the naturally radioactive elements. It was this work which brought him the Nobel Prize for Chemistry in 1908. And then, in his twelve years at Manchester, came his discovery of the central, small, but massive nucleus of the atom, and his co-operation with his brilliant Danish pupil, Niels Bohr, which produced the plan of the atom with its nucleus and planetary electrons. And just before he left Manchester he had made, with the simplest apparatus, experiments showing the possibility of causing an artificial disintegration of atoms of nitrogen. But during these great years I met Rutherford but seldom, and never on a footing to impress the meeting on my memory. There are, however, detailed reminiscences of Rutherford in his Montreal and Manchester periods on record, by men who had the privilege not only of close personal friendship with him in those years, but of the greater intimacy which comes from scientific collaboration. The late Professor Eve, to whom we owe the standard biography, was Rutherford's intimate colleague at Montreal, while Dr. Marsden, before he became Secretary of your Department of Industrial and Scientific Research in New Zealand, had been Rutherford's trusted assistant at Manchester. Dr. Marsden has given a vivid account of his great leader in those years, in his recent "Rutherford Memorial Lecture" to the Physical Society of London.

The first occasion of my meeting Rutherford again, of which I have a clear memory, must have been in 1920, soon after he had succeeded J. J. Thomson as Cavendish Professor. Some business had taken me to Cambridge and, using an "old boy's" privilege to dine in Trinity College, I encountered Rutherford in the Fellows' Combination Room. I wondered a little how much he might have changed, in the twenty-two years of his development from a research student into a world scientist of great and growing fame. Talk turned, almost inevitably, on what had become a prominent item of news in the press of the world—the confirmation of Einstein's general theory of relativity, by observations made during a solar eclipse, and before the first World War had come to

an end. "Well," said Rutherford, "I don't believe there are more
than about six people in the whole world who really understand
what that Einstein theory means." And, when I meekly enquired
who might be the other five, he looked at me quizzically for a
moment, and then, with a gust of laughter—"Good lord!
Dale," he exclaimed, "you don't suppose that I understand it, do
you?" Without doubt it was the same old Rutherford. Sir
James Jeans used to warn me not to take Rutherford too seriously
when he disclaimed understanding of mathematical conceptions.
Rutherford, he said, was a much better mathematician than he
chose to admit. We all knew, however, that he did not, in fact,
take interest in mathematical theories for their own sake, but
only in so far as they opened up new opportunities of experiment
to verify them. I well remember him after a dinner at the Royal
Society's dining club—he was apt on these occasions to be even
freer than at other times from hampering inhibitions—giving
his views on the conceptions of the universe as a whole, put
forward by rival mathematicians. "We have had four different
theories about it in the last ten years," he exclaimed; "and what
do you suppose will be left of any of them in another twenty?
What we want is more experimental facts, and by gad, you
fellows, I'm going to try to get them!" And, indeed, he and the
wonderful team which had gathered round him in the Cavendish
Laboratory were getting them at a tremendous pace. R. H.
Fowler, who became his son-in-law and was close to him in
intimate confidence, tells us that Rutherford was highly excited
and delighted by the laboratory's triumphs, as well he might
have been. At Montreal he had untangled the mysterious
phenomena of natural radio-activity, at Manchester he had
discovered the atomic nucleus and provided the basis for the plan
of atomic structure, and now, at Cambridge, he was able to see
rapid progress in the artificial disintegration and transmutation
of elements—the "Newer Alchemy," as he called it in his last
book.

I had the good fortune to see more of him than ever before
when he was President of the Royal Society, from 1925 to 1930,
as I was one of the Secretaries. Not long after that period came
what R. H. Fowler described as the *annus mirabilis* of atomic
physics, 1932, when Chadwick was led by his work with
Rutherford to discover the neutron, Anderson in Pasadena

discovered the "positron," and was early confirmed in that discovery by Blackett at Cambridge, and Cockcroft and Walton first demonstrated the artificial disintegration of the atomic nuclei of a light metal (lithium), when it was bombarded with greatly accelerated protons. I well remember Rutherford's opening speech at a discussion meeting of the Royal Society at about that time, in which he made what was probably a first general announcement of Cockcroft and Walton's highly important results. Looking round the room he said: "Cockcroft and Walton must be here somewhere. Stand up, you boys, and let them see what you look like!" The informality, which abated nothing of dignity when dignity was needed, and the friendly impulse to ensure that young men, though working under his inspiration, should get the full credit for what their skill and ingenuity had achieved, were alike characteristic of Rutherford. Working and leading in a field in which knowledge was progressing at breath-taking speed, into which other workers in different countries soon began to press eagerly, so that there were ever-present possibilities of overlap or forestalment, Rutherford never, to my knowledge, engaged in any dispute, or asserted any claims to credit or priority, even with regard to lines of research and discovery where friends, on his behalf, were inclined to resent and to resist what they regarded as encroachment by others. He seemed always too big to be bothered by, or even interested in, questions of property in scientific knowledge; he wanted to see the truth grow, and was prepared to welcome contributions from any source to its enlargement.

Rutherford used to tell me that, though he held his Cavendish Chair under statutes which imposed no age limit, he intended to retain it till he was 70, and then to make way for a younger man. Certainly he showed no sign of any abatement of his mental energy or his tremendous physical vigour, right up to his death, after a short illness due to a surgical accident, at the age of 66. "I want to leave £100 to Nelson College," were almost his last words to his wife. A whole world was in mourning for him, and testimonies came from all directions, to the simple grandeur of his personal character, as well as to his scientific triumphs. "Rutherford never made an enemy or lost a friend," said one who had known him long and intimately. "I never thought of Rutherford as a clever man," said Niels Bohr to me a few years ago; "he was much more than that—one of the few really great men." Several compared his epoch-making achievement in science to that of Newton—"Rutherford was the Newton of the atom," said more than one; and in 1939, when German scientists, under the Nazi rule and with the shadow of war advancing, had to be careful of their words, I heard his pupil Otto Hahn, speaking in London, say that "German scientists think of Ernest Rutherford as probably the greatest figure in science that the world has produced since Isaac Newton." Rutherford was lost to us at a time when we and all the world most surely needed the strength of his wisdom and the guiding power of his genius. The world was nearer then than any had believed, to the practical realization of further discoveries in Rutherford's nuclear physics—discoveries which were to make it possible for human agency to initiate the fission of atomic nuclei as a chain reaction, and thus to release the enormous energy known to be bound in their structure, but regarded, till then, as possibly for ever inaccessible to man. The world is now faced with the problem of ensuring the use of this gigantic new source of power, only for enlarging the material opportunities of human well-being and happiness, and of preventing its further use for destruction—for the destruction, perhaps, of all that civilization has painfully been building since before the dawn of history. And such a world may well feel orphaned by the loss from its councils, before his due time, of this great son of New Zealand, whose life and achievements had placed him among the few great ones, in all the long history of man's effort to understand the material universe in which he has his being.

MEDICINE, YESTERDAY
AND TO-MORROW*

I SUPPOSE that it would be difficult to justify on grounds of
mere reason the instinct which prompts us to find some
special significance in the beginning or the end of a century,
or of one of its simpler fractions. We must all be conscious,
however, of a strong impulse to indulge, upon such occasions, in
audits and forecasts, to look backwards and forwards, "to paint
the future from the past." And I am only too well aware that
this tendency to reminiscence and prediction, felt by the majority
at these rather long intervals, is apt to become a tiresome addiction, a disease of occupation, or perhaps I ought to say of retire-
ment, in those of us who have entered life's later years. I cannot,
therefore, ignore the fact that I myself, on more than one recent
occasion, have already written and even lectured about changes
and prospects in medicine, in that reminiscent vein.

And now I find myself yielding once again to persuasion, and
undertaking to address yet another audience on "Medicine,
Yesterday and To-morrow." I can only plead, in extenuation,
that I was concerned last year with the ending of a half-century,
and that now I am asked to commemorate the ending of a whole
one, in connexion with the Festival of Britain; and, further, that
I have addressed my earlier surveys to wholly medical audiences,
whereas I have been told to expect the presence of some to-day
who, though they must be credited with a lively interest in the
progress and the achievements of medicine, past and prospective,
have not been trained to familiarity with its technical details or
with the obscurer ranges of its terminology—the language in
which we medical men try to hide our mysteries from the laity,
and sometimes, perhaps, our ignorance from ourselves. I shall
try, then, to show you my picture of "Medicine, Yesterday and
To-morrow" in broad and simple outlines, and to lapse as seldom

---

* Lecture in connection with the Festival programme organized jointly by the
British Medical Association and the Royal Society of Medicine, delivered on
20th June, 1951, in the Great Hall, B.M.A. House.

as may be into the special dialect of the wards and the laboratories. You will have in mind, of course, the link between this lecture and the Festival of Britain, which must be held to extend the "yesterday" of which I speak as far back as 100 years ago; "to-morrow," on the other hand, may stand for only so much of the future as we may judge to lie within the limits of sane prediction.

MEN OF VISION

Albert, the Prince Consort, with the group of his distinguished advisers, and the Great Exhibition which they had planned with him 100 years ago, stand for us as symbols of that expectant age. They seem to have had a vision of mankind being led by science and the arts to new heights of material prosperity, of wide channels of commerce opened between the nations, and of a spirit of friendly rivalry aroused among all the peoples of the world. Evidence of these generous aspirations can be found in the plans which soon took shape in their hands, and are still effective, for applying the large earnings of their exhibition to the further promotion of science and the arts. We picture them thus watching the dawn of that scientific era of civilization in which we are still living; and we may surmise that, if they could see what has come of their vision, their reactions would be of amazement at seeing advances in many directions so far beyond any which they could have imagined, or even understood, and of sad disillusionment at finding us still so far from any certain prospect of the perpetual peace which they had believed that their enterprise would help to inaugurate—"the thousand years of peace" which the poet of their era, Alfred Tennyson, had so confidently bidden the bells to ring in at the new year.

And as we think of these men of vision, foreseeing thus early what the practical uses of science might be able to do for mankind, it seems the more remarkable to find so little evidence in their day of any comparable movement in medicine. Did the Prince and his advisers, one wonders, have any prevision of the transformation which science was to produce, in much later years, over the whole range of medical thought and practice? It does not seem likely; there was little enough then, indeed, to encourage any such prediction. For I think that we must admit that by 1851 medicine had shown remarkably little real progress even for several hundred years. The world, and our own country indeed, had produced at rather wide intervals great men of medicine who were also great men of experimental science; we had had William Harvey in the seventeenth century and John Hunter in the eighteenth. And when Edward Jenner made his empirical discovery of vaccination at the end of the eighteenth century he had unwittingly sown seeds, long to remain dormant, of our modern knowledge of immunity and of the viruses. Some of the discoveries of such men had been absorbed into the routine of medical practice; but they had achieved remarkably little yet towards the establishment of the progressive experimental tradition in medicine which was to have its real beginning and growth only much later, in times which most of us can remember.

Let us glance a little more closely at the state of medical and surgical knowledge in 1851. Anaesthesia was then still something of a novelty. Ether had first been given for an operation in Boston, Mass., in 1846, and Simpson had put forward chloroform as a more potent anaesthetic agent in the following year. The use of chloroform in childbirth, with which Simpson had been largely concerned, was still not accepted without protest on moral and religious grounds; and it was something of a triumph for its advocates when chloroform was first given to Queen Victoria in 1853 in one of her confinements. We ought further to remember, I think, that Morton's first public use of ether in surgery, of which the centenary was celebrated in Boston five years ago, was really the adoption in practice of recommendations which had been made from outside the medical pale by our own great discoverers, Davy and Faraday, forty-six and twenty-eight years earlier.

We may think, in any case, of anaesthesia, though still of a relatively crude type, as already available in 1851 for surgeons who had the enterprise to use it; so that patients in increasing numbers could already be relieved from the immediate pain of such operations as were yet regarded as justifiable. The range of these was still kept small, however, and the outcome of those performed was rendered very doubtful, by the septic complications which were still regarded then as a natural and practically inevitable consequence. We must remember that the discoveries of Louis Pasteur were then still in the future, and that it was not till 1865 that Lister's application of them to surgery began to reveal the infection of wounds by bacteria as the cause of suppuration and sepsis, and thus to provide one of the conditions for all the further progress of surgery.

DAWNING INTEREST IN HYGIENE

And, of course, there was no more knowledge in 1851 of the real nature of infectious diseases of any kind. A little earlier Edwin Chadwick and Southwood Smith had begun, in the face of much opposition, to stir the public conscience about matters of simple, common decency in hygiene. John Simon, who was eventually to become the first medical adviser to the Privy Council and then to the Local Government Board, had been appointed Medical Officer to the City of London in 1848. The reports which he promptly began to issue on the sanitary scandals of the city will always hold a special place among official documents, for their brilliant candour and their arresting eloquence. Simon was an acute observer and a powerful advocate. Another pioneer in that line, John Snow, traced an epidemic to the drinking of water from a particular pump, and even stopped it by having the handle removed; but neither of these knew anything, or could yet know anything, of the bacteria which made the water infective, and which, indeed, were only beginning to be separately identified more than thirty years later.

Typhoid was endemic here, of course, then and long afterwards, and cholera still swept across Europe in epidemics every ten years or less from its endemic centre in Asia; but few thought of any human agency as able to avert these dangers. My own father used to recall, from his boyhood, the cholera epidemic of 1854, and how men were then talking of the sensation created by John Bright when, speaking of its coming, he had laid a hush of fear upon the House of Commons: "The Angel of Death," he had told them, "has been abroad throughout the land. You may almost hear the beating of his wings." But Bright, with his Quaker eloquence, aroused no thought of resistance to the peril by means other than prayer and nursing.*

---

* When this lecture was first published (*Brit. Med. J.* 1951, ii, p. 1), a friend (the Rt. Hon Walter Elliot) did me the kindness of indicating errors in this statement—in the precise wording, here corrected, of Bright's rhetorical gesture, and in the immediate aim imputed to it. Of course I ought not to have quoted on the unchecked authority of two boyhood memories—my father's, as

We get a vivid impression of the helplessness of medical ignorance in dealing with such infectious diseases, not only in 1851, but for at least two following decades, when we recall that Albert, the Prince Consort, himself died of typhoid fever in 1861, at the age of 42, when he had only begun to give earnest of all that he might have done for this country, for Europe, and for the world; and that his eldest son, later King Edward VII, nearly died of the same disease in 1871, so that we only just escaped the further loss of all that he lived to achieve, with his very different and more readily popular gifts. Think of the outcry, of the fury of investigation, which would be aroused to-day by such a succession of hygienic catastrophes occurring to members of any of the world's ruling families or circles or, indeed, to any person well known to the public and the Press; how the experts, armed with all the latest devices for screening and testing, would swoop on every item of the food and water supplies, and on every potential human carrier in the entourage! And, if the search was not quickly successful, what an agitation would now arise for the immediate promotion of research on the problem! The thought of their late President, Franklin Roosevelt, crippled in his vigorous young manhood by poliomyelitis, has made such an emotional appeal to the citizens of the U.S.A. that funds for the support of research on that one disease have flowed there in almost embarrassing abundance.

The outstanding difference between then and now is that, in 1851, 1861, 1871, and even later, nobody had yet thought that research might discover the cause of such a disease as typhoid fever and ways of dealing with it—the way to cut off the cause of it at the source, or, if this should not succeed, to protect the individual by giving him an artificial resistance; or, again, if this should for any reason be lacking, to deal directly with the infection in the patient. We have now the knowledge and the means for effective action with various diseases at all these stages; but there was nothing then even to foreshadow what was to come. The work of Pasteur was needed, of course, before it could begin,

---

transmitted much later through my own! Bright was, in fact, offering support in 1855 to a move for ending the Crimean War, and ignoring the much heavier mortality in England from the cholera then raging, as well as from commoner epidemics, all of which he and his hearers would have regarded as visitations of Providence, and as beyond prevention by any act of man.

and that of Robert Koch, and of the great army of their followers to carry it forward.

PREVENTIVE AND OTHER MEDICATION

Eberth discovered the typhoid bacillus nearly thirty years after the Great Exhibition, in 1880; its identification was fully established by the middle of that decade, and protective inoculation with a suspension of the dead bacilli was introduced by Almroth Wright towards the end of the century, though not in time for such a novelty to have any important effect on the disastrous prevalence of typhoid fever in the Boer War. We were well into the present century before the part played by healthy carriers of pathogenic bacteria in the spread of this and other infections was clearly recognized; and it is only much later again, in the past few years indeed, that there has at last been definite promise, with the discovery of some of the more recent antibiotics, of a direct and effective treatment of the typhoid infection, in a patient who, in spite of all preventive precautions, has already been attacked.

Mention of such curative medication brings a reminder that we have still to look at the position of medicinal treatment in 1851. We have seen how few were the possibilities of surgical operation at that time, and it can be said without hesitation that the really effective medicinal treatments then available for the physician to prescribe were at best no more numerous. There were a few specifically active medicines which had been handed down from earlier centuries—mercury, which had been used since the end of the fifteenth century, cinchona and ipecacuanha, brought from South America in the seventeenth century, and digitalis, introduced by Withering's famous book, *An Account of the Fox-glove*, in 1785. These and a few others have survived even to the present day, as have also some of the drastic purgatives; these last, though rarely given now, having played a very prominent part in the practice of those physicians who favoured what was called a "reducing" treatment.

But, while there were then already a few drugs in use which had genuine activity, the true nature of the actions even of these, and the proper methods of using them, have been revealed only by much later advances of knowledge; others, as we have seen, were then given in a dosage so heroic as to be injurious rather then remedial. On the other hand, a large proportion of the drugs and medicaments used in those early days had actions vaguely defined and doubtfully existent. Medicinal treatment, in fact, was hardly ever given then with any idea that it could suppress or remove the cause of a disease. The usual aim was rather to build up the strength of the patient, or to weaken a supposed excess of his reaction, or otherwise to ease his symptoms by actions vaguely conceived and described as tonic, or relaxing, or sedative, or even alterative, and, frankly, to leave the essential cure to the *vis medicatrix naturae*.

It is not, of course, to be suggested that such symptomatic treatment had never any value, or that it has none even now: until a fuller knowledge can provide a remedy which can be shown to deal directly with the cause of an ailment, it is a plain duty of the physician to give any treatment which may be expected to maintain the patient's strength, to keep him comfortable and confident, and thus to leave nature with as free a hand as possible to eliminate the cause and effect the cure. We cannot, on the other hand, ignore the wide opening which a medicinal treatment with no other objective than this offered to self-delusion, oracular posturing, and benevolent humbug. It cannot be doubted, I think, that the prevalence of this attitude in the middle years of the nineteenth century, and later, brought medicinal treatment into low repute with the less easily credulous among the patients upon whom it was practised, as well as with the candid and critical among the physicians themselves. There was but little change in this situation, indeed, till after the end of the nineteenth century, and we owe the newer types of treatment, dealing in various ways but always directly with the different causes of disease, almost entirely to the advances of knowledge which have been made since the present century began, and very largely in its few most recent decades.

In turning now to consider some of the remarkable transformations which this and, indeed, almost every other aspect of medical knowledge and practice have since undergone, and largely in our own times, I must be careful not to imply that every kind of progressive activity in medicine was in complete abeyance 100 years ago. A few medical discoveries of major importance were then being made, as they are still, though at rather wide intervals, by the patient study of conditions which could be observed and characterized in the patient during life and of the regular association of these with changes found in the different organs after death. The advancement of knowledge by this slow, patient method, which waits for nature to perform her ruthless experiments and to present the results for our study, was indeed one of the special glories of medicine in those middle years of the nineteenth century; and we can proudly claim that in men like Richard Bright, Thomas Addison and others, we had British exponents of this method as great in their achievement as any whom the world has at any time produced.

BEGINNINGS OF MODERN ENDOCRINOLOGY

Let us choose, then, for particular mention and centenary celebration the first publication by Thomas Addison, in 1849, of a note on his discovery by such methods of the condition caused by degenerative disease of the suprarenal capsules, which is now known as Addison's disease; and his further publication in 1855, in a slender quarto pamphlet, of classically complete descriptions not only of this disease but, incidentally, of another and entirely different one which we now know as pernicious or Addison's anaemia. And I choose these two modest but remarkably perfect publications by Addison, not long before and not long after the year of the Great Exhibition, because I think that we can properly find in them the real starting point for the developments leading eventually to all our modern knowledge of the significance of the ductless glands, modern endocrinology, with all that it has meant for the recognition and treatment, in our own day, of so many conditions now known to be due to endocrine deficiencies.

This is not the occasion for more than a hasty glance at outstanding events in that remarkable chapter of medical history. Against a background of laboratory researches, on lines for which Addison's discovery forty years earlier had thus supplied the initiating stimulus, Murray, in Newcastle in 1891, first successfully treated an endocrine deficiency, myxoedema, with thyroid gland; and this was not only the first clinical application of endocrinology, but a very early example, at least, of the direct application, in treating the cause of a disease, of a discovery made largely in the experimental laboratories. Then, after another thirty years' interval filled largely with discouragement and frustration, came Banting and Best's discovery of insulin, and therewith not only health and efficiency for the previously doomed victims of diabetes, but a new spirit of optimism and enterprise in exploring other practical possibilities of endocrinology.

So before long we saw Addison's pernicious anaemia also yield at last to treatment with liver substance and extracts; and recently came the isolation of the active principle deficient in that disease and its recognition as a complex organic compound containing cobalt. Extracts containing hormones of the parathyroid gland and of the suprarenal cortex were prepared and brought into use, and a whole series of hormones from the anterior lobe of the pituitary body and from the sex glands, several from the latter being isolated and even made by artificial synthesis. And, more recently again, we have had the identification and preparation by synthesis of a range of pure hormones of different actions from the organ which Addison was studying 100 years ago, when he observed the progressive and fatal disease which was always associated with its degeneration—the cortex of the suprarenal capsules. And now we have the therapeutic applications of some of these cortical hormones and, alternatively, of a hormone from the anterior pituitary lobe which stimulates the suprarenal cortex to secrete them. And this treatment of rheumatoid conditions, and of others which seem in general to be due perhaps to excess, or to perversion, of the protective reactions with which the healthy tissues normally respond to various kinds of injury—these uses of the suprarenal hormone cortisone and of the corticotrophic pituitary hormone are already so full of beneficent promise that even now they are exciting immense interest and impatient eagerness for further knowledge of their uses and their limitations, not only among medical men but in much wider circles.

PROGRESS IN ANAESTHESIA

To take another example, I spoke of anaesthesia with ether and chloroform as still a novelty in 1851; and it is remarkable, in retrospect, to note that there was hardly any progress in this important service to surgery and obstetrics, apart from minor improvements in details of administration, till well into the present century. When I entered hospital as a student in 1900 the standard technique was still a fold of lint over the patient's face, on to which chloroform was delivered, drop by drop, as needed. It seems to me now, however, that there is no department of medical activity in which improvement has recently been more rapid and dramatic than in this of anaesthesia, mainly during the past two decades, and especially, indeed, in the more recent of these. Anybody who has had personal experience of anaesthesia for an important operation twenty or thirty years ago, and again in quite recent years, could tell of the magnitude of the change. Pharmacology and synthetic chemistry have been called in aid, together with experimental physiology, which in 1851 had only just entered upon its modern period of rapid development in Europe, from which it spread to Britain some twenty years later. So that now we have basal anaesthetics to prepare the way for those of deeper effect; curarine from the South American arrow-poison, bugbear of the Victorian sentimentalists but now beneficently used, with a growing range of synthetic substitutes, to cause muscular relaxation and so to reduce the dosage and increase the safety of the essential anaesthetic; and, most recently, synthetic substances which, by their action on sympathetic ganglia, lower the arterial blood pressure and enable a postural adjustment of the patient to produce a practically bloodless field of operation. Advances such as these clearly contribute to the amazing achievements of modern surgery in dealing with the brain, the lungs, and now even with the heart, its valves and its great vessels.

RADIOLOGY

An entirely new gift to the resources of surgery first, and then equally to those of medicine, was made by the discovery of X-rays in 1895 and then of radioactivity in 1896. These discoveries opened up, indeed, an immense and still expanding range of new knowledge to physics, the boundaries of which, as even I can remember, had till then appeared to have been so finally fixed and determined. And I think that we may find an early sign of the great change, which was then still to come, in the relation between practical medicine and the experimental sciences—a first break, as it were, in the high hedge which had so long been maintained between the two—in the impulse, which was almost immediately manifest, to put these new physical discoveries to medical uses. And that impulse has lasted till to-day, when in making more widely available the newest resources of atomic physics, whether in machines or in radioactive isotopes, the needs of medicine, whether for diagnosis, treatment, or progressive research, are being given a high priority as a matter of course.

IMMUNOLOGY

The effects on medicine of the coming and the development of bacteriology, and of its offshoots dealing with immunity and with the invisible viruses, would now need many books, whole libraries, to present them in detail; here a passing reference must serve. I have already spoken briefly of the revolutionary changes which they have made possible in the diagnosis of infectious diseases, in the tracing of infections to their sources, and in the new creation therewith of large aspects of preventive medicine and new possibilities for the promotion of public health by law and administration. I ought still to give further emphasis, in passing, to the advances produced in curative treatment, as well as in individual protection, by the scientific study of immunity, which Jenner's vaccination had foreshadowed and Pasteur and his school had developed, but which had its effective beginning as a separate branch of science, immunology, in that remarkable last decade of the nineteenth century, during which the invisible viruses were also first clearly recognized. The first of the anti-toxins, for the treatment of diphtheria and other infections, were such a gift of the 1890s. Some of them still hold a high place among the remedies which directly remove the cause of a disease or arrest its progress. A more recent development, however, and one to be greatly welcomed, makes it now possible largely to forestall the need for such curative treatment by actively immunizing in advance of exposure to an infection those liable to the risk of it. It is no longer an aspiration, but in certain advanced communities in the New World a matter of demonstration, that diphtheria can thus be eliminated altogether; and we ought to do it here. The possibility of a similarly effective protection against tetanus was demonstrated in the second world war.

PREVENTION

The proverbial recognition of prevention as better than cure applies not only to these uses of immunology but equally to the uses in medicine of other kinds of scientific discovery. Take for example that of the vitamins—one of the great gifts to practical medicine made by biochemistry, which itself, as a separate discipline, is a creation of the twentieth century. The use of vitamin D to treat rickets after that disease has appeared is already, in this country, an obsolescent anomaly. Rickets, which till so recently was a pathetic commonplace in the children of our industrial communities, disappeared in a few years when the nature of the dietary defect responsible for it had been discovered just over thirty years ago. We have almost forgotten its former threat to the physique and the health of our children. Even twenty years ago, when a pure vitamin D was first prepared, it had already become difficult to find cases of rickets for its trial in the clinic. And we may take this prevention of causes rather than the treatment of their results as the proper ultimate aim of medical policy, not only in dealing with other diseases due to shortages of other vitamins in the diet—scurvy, pellagra, beri-beri—but even in planning further researches on those which are due to deficiencies of hormones. Though we have now a great army of diabetic patients to show us daily that continuous treatment with insulin enables them to lead a nearly normal life, it would obviously be still better if we could find a way to prevent the deficiency, by arresting or reversing the injury to the pancreatic islets at its beginning, or even by anticipating its occurrence.

A very rapid epitome of the history of another disease during the century we are commemorating will further illustrate several factors in the transformation of the medical outlook which it has witnessed, as well as the accelerating tempo of the change. The first diagram in Sir Allen Daley's recent Purvis Oration, published in the *British Medical Journal* (June 9, p. 1279), shows at a glance that typhus fever must still have been dreaded as a recurrent scourge in the London of 1851, and that it ranked as a major cause of death in its outbreaks for many years after that. Then it almost disappeared, with no assignable reason except the general improvement in living conditions and sanitation. When I was a student, in 1900, a message reported the admission of an odd case of typhus to one of the London fever hospitals, and offered the rare opportunity of seeing what was by then becoming a medical curiosity in London. Between then and the first world war, however, evidence appeared showing that typhus was one of a group of infectious fevers transmitted from animals to man or from man to man by the bites of insects and other arthropods, and that epidemic typhus was carried from man to man by the body louse; so that the disappearance of typhus with rising standards of personal cleanliness, and its known tendency to break out in armies at war and in populations overtaken by the famine and devastation which a war leaves in its wake, all began to become clear. Then during the first world war the minute organism, *Rickettsia*, responsible for this louse-borne typhus, was discovered and the manner of its transmission was studied in detail. In the second world war, as soon as the potent insecticide D.D.T. became available, a threatened epidemic of typhus was stopped by the use of this agent on a louse-infested population. There remained, however, other rickettsial diseases belonging to the typhus group; and one in particular, carried from jungle rats to man by an almost invisible mite, caused a heavy mortality among our armies in Burma, and a serious threat even to the outcome of that campaign. No known insecticide could deal with the transmitter of the jungle typhus; but now, since the war, it has been found that one, at least, of the new antibiotic remedies, chloramphenicol, will rapidly eradicate a rickettsial infection which has already become established, and produce a prompt recovery of the patient. So another group of the great enemies to human life has been driven back to its last line of resistance, and beaten there.

A PAGEANT OF PROGRESS

While, then, we may accept prevention rather than cure as an ultimate aim, we are bound also to recognize that, so far as we can foresee, the curative and even the symptomatic treatment of diseases which it has as yet been impossible to prevent, diseases of infection as well as diseases of deficiency, will still be a major obligation in the practice of medicine. And it is obvious to everybody, I think, to patients and the public at large as well as to medical men, that there has been no greater transformation in medicine during recent years than in the direct efficacy of the medicinal treatment which research has now made available for many diseases. The story of the triumphs of chemotherapy, conceived and inspired by the genius of Paul Ehrlich and effectively launched early in the twentieth century, has now been told so often that we need only remind ourselves here of a few of the milestones, or signposts for new lines of advance, on the course of what has indeed become a majestic pageant of progress. We think of "salvarsan," discovered in 1909, "germanin" (suramin) during the first world war, and the first synthetic remedies for malaria, most fortunately, before the second. In 1935, after long waiting, came the first specific remedies for the more familiar bacterial infections—sulphonamide derivatives, the "sulpha-drugs" in popular parlance; and then the use of penicillin, a British discovery worthy, we may well think, of a festival of its own; and now the other antibiotics in a still lengthening series. The change in the therapeutic prospect, in what the doctor can be expected to do for an illness, has been truly revolutionary. Not long ago a friend of mine, just recovered from an acute pneumonia under modern treatment, told me that he had come now to think of pneumonia—that "Captain of the Men of Death," as Sir William Osler called it not many years ago—as less troublesome on the whole than a common cold. "You see," he said, "they can really do something to cure a pneumonia now." And I believe that that represents a not uncommon attitude. The doctor's medicinal treatment is no longer, as it was in 1851 and even till the end of the nineteenth century, a subject chiefly for a grim kind of ridicule, which—let us be candid—much of it then deserved. The tendency is rather to go to the other ex-treme, to demand immediate miracles and to make it almost a cause of grievance that there should still be diseases for which medical research has not yet been able to find effective means of prevention or cure. "When," they ask us now, "is medical re-search going to find something really effective against influenza or poliomyelitis?"

Nobody, of course, can say when; only to-morrow can give that answer; but we have abundant ground, from analogies with what has already happened with many other diseases, for a pre-diction that also in the case of diseases like influenza and polio-myelitis, due to infections by viruses, effective means of pre-ventive or curative treatment will eventually be discovered. We may remind ourselves, perhaps—though there is no great force in this analogy—that in more than one earlier instance, such as those of insulin and of the sulphonamide series, there seems to have been an interval of rather more than thirty years between the appearance of a reasonable basis for endeavour and the achievement of a decisive discovery. I was privileged to watch the discovery of the influenza virus in 1933 by good colleagues of mine; and I wonder whether those of you who live so long will have to wait till after 1963 to see that discovery made fully effective for the control of the disease. Who can say? We can only surmise that, with knowledge of the nature of the viruses so rapidly advancing, now that they can be cultivated on developing eggs, spun down with an ultracentrifuge, seen and photographed with an ultramicroscope, a practical fruition may yet come much earlier.

I have selected only some of the more vivid examples from a large range open to choice. In loyalty to my own special craft of physiology, and to British physiology in particular, I might have spoken of its far-reaching influence on all our knowledge of the functions and disorders of digestion and excretion, circulation and respiration. I can only pause to ask you to let your thoughts turn for a moment, in a tribute of respect, to a great British master in that field, Sir Charles Sherrington, born only six years after the Great Exhibition, and still living to see the spreading influence of his work, his teaching and his example, on all modern progress in our knowledge of the normal workings of the nervous system and of departures therefrom.

TO-MORROW

Looking more widely at the position and the progress of effective medical knowledge as a whole to-day, I see no sign that the rate of its advance is becoming slower, that it is yet approaching anything like a climax or the crest of a wave. Everything seems, on the contrary, to point to its continuing, even with an increasing acceleration, into any to-morrow that we can foresee. If I gave rein to my imagination I might easily find myself involved in all kinds of prophetic fantasies. But I think that I ought rather to use the few minutes which are left to me in asking you to consider what we are going to do to-morrow, with all this new and potentially life-saving knowledge which is pouring now, and will continue to pour in a swelling flood, from the laboratories and the clinics. It must surely be a matter of first concern to us who are medical men, and not only to us but also to the members of the public whom many of you serve as your patients, to be assured that all this new knowledge, without avoidable delay, can be put to its proper use for the common good, for the saving of life, the assuagement of suffering, whether bodily or mental, and the promotion of the general health.

I am no politician myself, medical or otherwise; but it has

seemed obvious to me for some time that the cost and the organization of all that would be needed for the fulfilment of that purpose would become too great a task for unaided individual enterprise in medical practice, and that the State would sooner or later have to give its assistance to enable that need of the community to be met. The State has supported medical research in this country since 1913, and is doing so to-day on a scale more than thirty times as great as that with which it began. I have heard no suggestion that this expenditure is too great or has been ill applied. And, since our State has assumed this predominant responsibility for supporting medical research, it was not unnatural, I think, to expect that support would also, in due course, be forthcoming from the State, to enable the wealth of new knowledge resulting from the medical research of all the world to be brought progressively to the aid of everybody needing it. Speaking in this Great Hall, I cannot be unaware of the many personal and professional difficulties and hardships entailed by a rapid adjustment to the new structure of medical practice which State action has now created and imposed. I am neither unmindful of these nor unsympathetic. But it seems to me that the success of whatever solution to these problems may be found must, in a longer view, be measured by the degree to which it will ease the all-important task of bringing the new and ever-growing resources of medical knowledge to the service of the individual patient and the community. It is by its success or its failure in meeting that, its primary obligation, that our National Health Service must stand to be judged at the bar of history; and we must wait for To-morrow to give the verdict.

THE MECHANISM OF
ANAPHYLAXIS*

I AM very proud and grateful to have been invited to take part in this historic occasion. It commemorates one of the great events in the history of Physiology and Pathology. It has been to me a matter of very great regret that I have been prevented, by a medical embargo, from making the journey to Paris, to take part in this commemorative ceremony; but I am fortunate in that Dr. Halpern has most kindly undertaken to read, on my behalf, the communication which I had hoped to be able to present here in person.

The interest of an occasion which would, in any case, have been a most notable one, is greatly enhanced by the fact that Professor Portier, who took part in the dramatic discovery of the anaphylactic reaction, and in the immediate recognition of its great and novel importance, is able to take a personal and prominent part in this celebration. You will have heard from him, I am sure, an account of the peculiar circumstances in which that discovery was made. The late Professor Charles Richet and he were experimenting with a naturally poisonous protein, "actinocongestine," which they had extracted from the tentacles of a sea-anemone. Having observed its action, when they injected it intravenously into dogs in different doses, they preserved the animals which had survived the smaller initial injections, and repeated the injections into these dogs after an interval of some weeks, expecting to find some degree of specific immunity to the poison already established, and to be able to enhance this in the familiar manner, by a series of increasing injections. Contrary to this expectation, the second injections, even of doses which at the first had produced but slight effects, evoked symptoms which, in the rapidity of their onset, their great severity, and their frequently fatal termination, appeared to be similar to those which had followed first injections

---

* The French version of this Address was presented at the celebration in Paris, on 10th May, 1952, of the discovery of Anaphylaxis, by Portier and Richet, fifty years earlier. The English version was first published in the Danish *Acta Allergologica*.

of the larger, lethal doses. The effect of the first injection, then, had apparently been, not the production of immunity, prophylaxis, but of the opposite condition, which they termed "anaphylaxis."

Nobody who had first seen this phenomenon, in the circumstances in which Portier and Richet thus discovered it, would have adopted a different interpretation of its nature. Yet it was not long before it became clear that such an explanation of its meaning was not compatible with other aspects of the phenomenon. In the years immediately following the initial discovery, the observations of Arthus on the rabbit, of Theobald Smith and of Rosenau and Anderson on the guinea-pig showed that a comparable, rigidly specific sensitiveness, or anaphylaxis, appeared in these species, as the result of a preliminary injection, a few weeks earlier, of normally innocuous foreign proteins, such as those in the blood serum of a horse or in the albumin of a fowl's egg. The reactions by which this sensitiveness was manifested in these different animal types, were, indeed, rather remarkably different from those described by Portier and Richet in their experiments on the dog; but it was soon made clear that this difference had no connexion with the natural toxicity of the substances with which the first observations had been made. For, in the dog also, which had received, a few weeks earlier, a preparatory injection of a naturally non-poisonous foreign protein, such as that of horse serum or egg-albumin, a reinjection of the same substance would elicit a reaction entirely comparable, in its nature and its violence, to that which Portier and Richet had first seen with a second injection of their actinocongestine.

Anaphylaxis, then, was not, as had seemed at first to be so obvious, a condition of acquired sensitiveness, or diminished resistance to a natural poison; it was a condition in which the animal responded to a previously injected foreign protein, even to a normally quite inactive one, as though it were, indeed, a powerful poison. And, in the years which followed, it often seemed to me that a great deal of fruitless effort might have been saved, and a great deal of confusion and needless controversy avoided, if all of the many investigators, who became engaged in the study of anaphylaxis and the mechanism of its production, had kept clearly in view this outcome of the observations made at these early stages of the investigation. Portier and Richet's initial observation was, in fact, not only sound in itself, but highly significant, when it was correctly interpreted in the light of further evidence. For it showed that the reaction of an animal, sensitized by a prior injection, to a further injection even of a normally inactive protein, had a close and even a deceptive resemblance to the reaction of a normal animal of the same species to a naturally poisonous protein—to any, indeed, of a large class of such poisons. Later we shall see that a similar syndrome may be produced by an even much wider range of poisonous substances, many of them not even of a protein nature. It ought, accordingly, to have been clear, even from a consideration of Portier and Richet's earliest experiments and of those which so quickly followed them, that it is not the syndrome of the shock which is characteristic of the anaphylactic condition; it is the sensitizing effect of a previous injection, which causes that syndrome to appear in response to the injection of a protein which would not normally have any such effect.

The type of reaction itself had, indeed, been known for many years as that given by the animal body, and by that of the dog in particular, to a whole group of naturally poisonous proteins, or to poisonous products obtained artificially, from naturally inert proteins, by partial hydrolytic cleavage. As long ago as 1880, Schmidt-Mülheim had described the reaction of the dog to the intravenous injection of a sufficient dose (about 0.3 gramme per kilogramme) of the so-called "Peptone" of Witte—a mixture of albumoses and peptones, obtained by the peptic digestion of blood-fibrin. He had observed the collapse of the arterial pressure, accompanied by a great congestion of the liver and the gastro-intestinal mucous membrane and, especially, the loss of the coagulability of the blood, which followed such an intravenous injection of peptone into a dog. And, quite early in the study of anaphylaxis, the effects produced by such injections of "peptone" in the dog and in other species, and particularly in the guinea-pig, had become a centre of attention. For the reaction of the anaphylactic guinea-pig to reinjection of the sensitizing antigen was rather strikingly different from that which was first seen in the dog. The dog had shown the syndrome long familiar as the effect of injecting peptone—circulatory collapse, intense and obstructive congestion of the liver, retrograde congestion of the gastro-intestinal canal with capillary haemorrhages, and loss by the blood of its normal power of clotting. The anaphylactic guinea-pig, on the other hand, responded to a reinjection of the antigen with a suffocating, valve-like constriction of the bronchioles, so that the animal characteristically died in a few minutes from asphyxia, with the lungs in a state of permanent distension— the so-called Auer-Lewis syndrome. It accordingly appeared to be highly suggestive, when Biedl and Kraus found that this previously unfamiliar reaction, shown by the anaphylactic guinea-pig in response to its antigen, was also reproduced in the normal guinea-pig by an intravenous injection of peptone. And it must be admitted that it was very natural that further investigations should proceed, for a time, on the assumption that the anaphylactic condition was due to the appearance in the blood, as the result of the first injection, of something which caused the sensitizing protein, when reinjected, to undergo a rapid, enzymatic hydrolysis, with a resulting production of a poisonous cleavage product of the "peptone" type, a non-specific "Apotoxine" (Richet) or "Anaphylatoxine." And then, when evidence had been obtained to show that the anaphylactic condition was due to the formation of an immune substance or antibody of some kind, and probably of a precipitin, the theory of the formation of an anaphylatoxin underwent a number of variations in detail. Some proponents of this theory supposed that a specific precipitate, formed in the blood when the sensitizing antigen was reinjected, was attacked by a natural protease of the blood, with a resulting formation of poisonous cleavage products; others, who distrusted this form of the theory from quantitative considerations, supposed that the formation of the precipitate would remove an antitryptic factor present in the normal blood, and thereby initiate an autolytic cleavage of the blood proteins in general, with the production from them, again, of poisonous cleavage products. Others, again, regarded the formation of a specific precipitate in the circulating blood as disturbing the delicate equilibrium between its plasma proteins and its formed elements, in a manner comparable to the effect produced by contact with a foreign surface; so that the blood was supposed to have become involved in the earlier phases of the coagulation process, and therewith to have acquired a toxicity responsible for the symptoms. Yet others supposed that the blood acquired toxicity from a more vaguely conceived disturbance of the colloidal solution of its plasma constituents.

It should be noted that, at this juncture, the guinea-pig appears to have become the experimental animal used in a very large proportion of the experiments on anaphylaxis. The dramatic and rapidly fatal reaction, the "Auer-Lewis syndrome," with which it responded to a reinjection of the sensitizing antigen, was a comparatively novel discovery; and it was peculiarly easy to overlook the true significance of Biedl and Kraus's experiments with peptone, which might properly have been taken to indicate that there was nothing in the syndrome itself which was characteristic of anaphylaxis. It was found that the fresh blood serum of a guinea-pig would readily acquire toxic properties under a variety of manipulations *in vitro*, enabling it to produce a reaction more or less closely reproducing the Auer-Lewis syndrome, when it was injected into the circulation of a normal guinea-pig. It was claimed, for example, that the serum acquired a toxicity of this supposedly significant kind, when it was incubated *in vitro* with suspensions of living or dead bacteria, of kaolin or Kieselguhr, or after emulsification with chloroform, or with sols of starch, inulin, or agar-agar. Only when it had been emulsified with chloroform was there clear evidence of proteolytic cleavage in the serum; and in that case the effect of its injection was to produce a massive intravascular clotting of the blood, with symptoms which only superficially recalled those seen in the anaphylactic shock. It must be admitted that it is not possible to offer complete explanations of the toxicity of all these preparations. Some of them did produce symptoms more definitely suggestive of, though in no case completely identical with, those of the anaphylactic reaction. In any case, however, those who devoted so much time and labour to the investigation of their properties seem to have wandered a long way from their initial objective. There was curiously little connexion, indeed, between the effects of these artificial "anaphylatoxins" on normal guinea-pigs, and the specific sensitiveness to a protein caused by an earlier small injection, or passively conferred, after a shorter interval, by injection of a specific precipitin for that protein, which was the true anaphylaxis. The only link, indeed, was in the resemblance, varying in degree, between the syndromes produced by the anaphylatoxins in normal guinea-pigs, and that seen in the anaphylactic reaction of the sensitized guinea-pig to the sensitizing antigen. And it cannot be too strongly insisted that there is nothing characteristic in this syndrome, which can be produced in the guinea-pig by a whole range of poisons, the actions of which have no proper connexion with anaphylaxis; just as we saw earlier that the very different syndrome, seen in the anaphylactic reaction of the dog, can be produced in normal dogs by a similarly wide variety of poisons. *It is not the syndrome which is anaphylactic; anaphylaxis is the production of a common syndrome by a special kind of immunological reaction.*

I have been obliged, by consideration of the time available on an occasion of this kind, to dismiss rather dogmatically this large volume of evidence on the artificial production of the so-called anaphylatoxins. And the need for brevity will oblige me to be at least as dogmatic, in presenting the evidence which seems to me to have a direct and positive significance, for an understanding of the nature, on the one hand, of the anaphylactic condition and, on the other hand, of the mechanism of the reaction of the anaphylactic animal to the protein to which it has been sensitized. The former of these problems is one of immunology, while the latter involves considerations proper to physiology and pharmacology as well.

THE NATURE OF THE ANAPHYLACTIC CONDITION

(a) *In the guinea-pig.* In my opinion, the nature of the true anaphylaxis in the guinea-pig was made clear by the immunological experiments of the late Richard Weil in 1913, in which he followed the development of passive anaphylaxis after an intravenous injection of a precipitin. Weil showed that the specific sensitiveness appeared in parallel with the disappearance of the precipitin from the blood. He found, further, that this sensitiveness was immediately masked, replaced by an immunity, when a further injection of precipitin was made into the circulation. Concurrently it was shown by Schultz, in Washington, and by myself in London, that the isolated plain muscle of an anaphylactic guinea-pig, freed in my own experiments from all traces of blood, reacts specifically to the sensitizing antigen. In experiments made with plain muscle of the uterus from young females, I was able to demonstrate *in vitro* all the main features of the anaphylactic condition in the guinea-pig—its exquisite specificity, its disappearance (desensitization) after reaction to an effective dose of the antigen, and its passive transfer by antibody. Later, with

C. H. Kellaway, I was able, with the same preparation, to demonstrate *in vitro* the immunity which Weil had demonstrated *in vivo*. We showed that the plain muscle, sensitized by an antibody fixed to its cells, could be completely protected from the effect of the antigen, when an excess of the same antibody was added to the fluid in which the preparation was suspended.

More recently my former colleague, Sir Percival Hartley, has shown how readily plain muscle from a normal guinea-pig can be made anaphylactically sensitive, by simply soaking it for 24–48 hours, in the cold, in a dilution of the appropriate antibody. It is then washed and suspended in a warm saline solution, to test the effect upon it of the corresponding antigen.

It seems to me that evidence such as this has proved beyond reasonable doubt, that anaphylaxis in the guinea-pig, causing it to die from a suffocating contraction of the plain muscle of the bronchioles when the antigen is reinjected, is due to the presence of an ordinary, precipitating antibody, abnormal only in its distribution, in that it is predominantly attached to the fixed cells of the tissues, and especially to those of the plain muscle, and present only in minor quantities in the circulating blood and body fluids.

Obviously this conception of anaphylaxis in the guinea-pig, as due to a predominantly cellular fixation of an ordinary antibody, is applicable only to soluble antigens. It clearly cannot be applied, for example, to what some observers have termed anaphylaxis to the blood corpuscles of another species. An intravascular haemolysis in the guinea-pig may, indeed, evoke symptoms resembling those of a true anaphylactic reaction in that animal. I feel obliged, however, again to insist that it is not the symptoms which are characteristic of anaphylaxis, but the conditions under which a common syndrome is evoked. And, from that point of view, it appears to me that we ought, in the interests of precision, to limit the application of the term anaphylaxis to the condition to which it was first applied and is still in most general use—the condition in which a previous injection of a soluble antigen has produced a specific sensitiveness to that substance.

(b) *In the dog.* In the dog, again, there is clear evidence, which was first obtained by Manwaring, to show that the condition of anaphylaxis is due to a predominant fixation of an antibody, presumably again a precipitin, to the fixed cells of a tissue. The cells in this case, however, are not those of plain muscle; on the contrary, the sensitization by antibody is concentrated in the dog on the cells of the liver. If the liver of an anaphylactic dog is excluded from the circulation, injection of the antigen into the bloodstream produces no shock; and if isolated preparations of plain muscle are made from an anaphylactic dog, they give no significant response to contact with the antigen. Nevertheless, when, with the liver in the circulation, the reinjected antigen has elicited the shock, the viscera and the blood vessels, and the blood itself, all become involved in the ensuing general syndrome. Some substances have been poured into the blood from the primarily affected liver cells, to produce these secondary effects on other organs; and we must consider a little later what these substances are.

(c) *In the rabbit.* In several ways, the phenomenon of anaphylaxis in the rabbit appears to differ from that in the other species. It is far less regular in its occurrence than in the guinea-pig. The Arthus phenomenon, a local reaction to injections of a foreign protein into or beneath the rabbit's skin, seems clearly to involve a local sensitization of the tissues, presumably by the fixation of a precipitating antibody. On the other hand, the conditions for the production of a passive anaphylaxis in the rabbit, and for the elicitation of a shock in such an animal by intravenous injection of the antigen, appear to be quite different from those seen in the guinea-pig. The optimum conditions for the production of the shock in the rabbit seem to be created, when a serum giving a specific precipitate with the antigen is injected intravenously, and the antigen soon after it, or even simultaneously; so that no interval is required, as in the guinea-pig, for the removal of the precipitin from the circulation and its predominant fixation in the tissues. The shock in the rabbit then—the evocation of which is, in any case, a comparatively capricious phenomenon—would appear to be due, most probably, to the interaction of the antigen with the specific precipitin in the circulating blood, and therein to present a sharp contrast to the anaphylactic shocks in the guinea-pig and the dog.

If we inquire why such a reaction in the blood should cause a shock-like reaction in the rabbit, it seems relevant to observe that the rabbit's blood is peculiarly rich in platelets, and that it is apparently the platelets in this species which normally contain nearly the whole of the singularly high content of histamine to be found in the rabbit's blood. To the significance of this we must turn our attention almost immediately. We may note here that the central feature of the syndrome, which has been called the anaphylactic shock in the rabbit, is an obstruction of the circulation through the lungs, leading to a failure of the right side of the heart in a state of distension; and that this lethal reaction accompanies an almost complete disappearance of the platelets from the blood, and the agglutination of the few which remain.

THE MECHANISM OF THE ANAPHYLACTIC SHOCK

It was in 1910 that the late P. P. Laidlaw and I, making a first study of the organic diamine, histamine, observed the remarkable resemblance between the different symptoms which it produced in the different species and those of the anaphylactic shock in the same species—collapse of the systemic circulation in the dog, suffocating constriction of the bronchioles and permanent pulmonary distension in the guinea-pig, and congestive failure of the right side of the heart in the rabbit. Not many months earlier Biedl and Kraus had drawn attention to the even more complete resemblance between the different symptoms produced by the Peptone-Witte, and those of the anaphylactic shock in the different species. Peptone had produced, in the dog, the obstructive congestion of the liver, retrograde congestion of the alimentary viscera, and the incoagulability of the blood seen also in the dog's anaphylactic shock, but absent from the actions of histamine. This defect in the otherwise remarkable resemblance made us hesitate to suggest any direct or causal relationships between the effects of histamine and the symptoms of the anaphylactic reaction. And this hesitation continued, until, about 1926, definite evidence began to become available of the presence of histamine as a natural constituent of the animal body, widely distributed in the cells of its active organs and tissues, held, apparently, in some inactivating association with the protoplasm of the living, uninjured cell, but readily liberated in active form from a cell exposed to even a slight injury of any kind. An intelligible conception thus began to emerge, of the anaphylactic shock as due, primarily, to a reaction of the reinjected antigen with a precipitating antibody which had become incorporated into tissue cells—especially into cells of the plain muscle in the guinea-pig and cells of the liver in the dog.

The consequent aggregating reaction, like any other kind of injury to the cell, would then immediately liberate physiologically active substances from their normally inactivating associations with the cell protoplasm; and since histamine would be by far the most active of these, the actions of histamine, with their special characters in the different species, would form the most conspicuous feature of the anaphylactic shock in each case. This conception soon received direct experimental confirmation. Feldberg and his co-workers, in Berlin, demonstrated the release of histamine, when the antigen was added to the saline fluid perfusing the lung of an anaphylactic guinea-pig; while Dragstedt and his co-workers, in Chicago, found that histamine appeared in the lymph flowing from the liver of an anaphylactic dog, when the shock was produced by injecting the antigen into the general circulation. And another feature, required to complete the picture of the anaphylactic shock but missing from the histamine syndrome, was supplied a few years later, when it was discovered that the primary injury of the liver cells in an anaphylactic dog, by contact with the antigen, or in those of a normal dog by contact with "peptone," caused them to pour into the general circulation, not only histamine, with the consequent general vasodilatation and spasms of visceral plain muscle, but also heparin, with the resulting loss of the coagulability of the blood. It is, of course, possible that a cellular antibody might be attached, not only to cells of the solid tissues, but to the leucocytes and platelets in the blood, where its presence, with that of histamine, might play a significant part in the genesis of the shock in certain species. And, with that additional possibility in mind, we may briefly consider the separate applications of this general conception to the anaphylactic reactions of different animal types.

(a) *In the guinea-pig.* The resemblance of the histamine action to the anaphylactic shock is particularly close in this species; and the fact that the release of histamine could be demonstrated when the antigen was applied to the anaphylactic plain muscle, isolated as completely as possible from other tissues, appeared to leave little doubt of its significance. Rocha e Silva, however, has recently observed that the histamine released from an isolated guinea-pig's lung, when the so-called "agar-anaphylatoxin" is added to the saline perfusion, is much greater in amount than that which is released from a similar preparation of the anaphylactic lung, when the specific antigen is perfused. He appears to argue from this that histamine from other sources than the sensitized plain muscle itself takes part in the anaphylactic shock in this species. The observation is interesting in itself, as evidence that the agar-treated serum thus releases histamine from the lung in the absence of blood; and it is to be presumed that the relatively large output of histamine thus evoked is mainly from the endothelium of the blood capillaries and the walls of the alveoli, of which the lung tissue, with its remarkably high content of histamine, is predominantly composed. The point of chief importance for our problem, however, is not the *quantity* of the histamine released, but its effectiveness in producing the constriction of the bronchioles which forms the central feature of the anaphylactic shock. And in the true anaphylactic shock, as Kellaway and I were able to demonstrate, the constriction of the bronchioles is much more forcible and complete than that produced by any of the anaphylatoxins, even though their effects may be accompanied by a much larger output of histamine, from other tissue cells, than that which is released, in the anaphylactic reaction, directly from the cells of the plain muscle itself. In the same connexion, it may be noted that the anaphylatoxins cause a practically complete disappearance of the platelets from the blood of the guinea-pig, while the specific antigen, in the true anaphylactic shock, has very little effect of that kind.

(b) *In the dog.* Although the anaphylactic reaction in the dog was the first to be observed—the historic event, indeed, which is commemorated on this occasion—it appears to me that there are details of the mechanism of its production which are yet incompletely understood. A primary reaction in the liver, with secondary effects due to portal obstruction, on the one hand, and to the liberation of products from the poisoned liver, histamine and heparin in particular—these are on evidence which seems to be convincing. Recent observations by Rocha e Silva and others, however, appear to me to show quite definitely, that the full reaction of the anaphylactic liver with the antigen involves the coöperation, not merely of the blood, but of the blood in its natural, coagulable condition. Only when both are present, the sensitized liver and the coagulable blood, can the specific antigen produce the full, intensely congestive reaction, with the resulting abundant output of histamine and heparin; but the evidence yet available appears to be inadequate to explain the nature of the contribution made by the blood to the full reaction.

(c) *In the rabbit.* As I have already suggested, the available evidence, concerning the phenomenon which has been described as the acute anaphylactic shock in the rabbit, suggests that the primary reaction may well take place in the blood. The rabbit's blood contains an unusual abundance of platelets, and these appear to be of a special kind and to contain a large proportion, at least, of the histamine in which, moreover, the rabbit's blood is peculiarly rich. There is direct evidence, indeed, that the addition, *in vitro*, of a specific antigen to the blood of a rabbit containing the corresponding antibody, causes a release of histamine from the cellular elements of the blood into the plasma. The distinction, indeed, between the anaphylactic and the immune conditions seems to be much less clearly defined in the rabbit than in the dog and, particularly, in the guinea-pig. The reaction which has been recognized as an anaphylactic shock in the rabbit may involve, therefore, a primary antigen-antibody reaction in the blood, with a release of histamine into its plasma and a resulting constriction of the pulmonary vessels, to the obstructive effect of which clumps of agglutinated platelets may also contribute— apart from any possibility of a direct sensitization of the pulmonary arterioles to the effect of the antigen.

CONCLUSION

Anaphylaxis, then, is not the opposite of immunity, as its discoverers naturally supposed when they observed a special manifestation of it. It is, on the contrary, a phase of immunity, in which a precipitating antibody is located in such a relation to living cells of the fixed tissues or, in certain cases, of the circulating blood, that its union with the reinjected antigen subjects the cells to a sudden injury. To this injury, as to injury of any kind, mechanical or chemical, these cells respond by the liberation of substances normally held in their protoplasm. Some of these substances have powerful physiological or pharmacodynamic actions, which appear when they are thus liberated; and conspicuous among such active substances are histamine and heparin, to the actions of which, as we have seen, we can attribute different phases of the anaphylactic syndrome, as this is observed in different species.

On such a conception of anaphylaxis, it is clear that there is nothing specific or characteristic about the syndrome, the association of symptoms seen in the anaphylactic shock. It is the production of that syndrome by an immunological reaction that identifies the shock as anaphylactic. A shock-reaction of the same general type can be produced in a variety of ways, and by a growing range of chemical substances; some of these are thrown out of solution, so as to form precipitates, when injected into the blood stream, and others so directly injure fixed tissue cells, as to provoke a sudden liberation from them of histamine; and thus have been produced reactions which those who observed them have described as "anaphylactoid reactions," "crises nitritoides," or "crises hémoclasiques."

Then there is the group of naturally acquired specific idiopathies, commonly termed "allergies," and most familiar in man. It seems to be beyond doubt that these are also due to specific antibodies, predominantly fixed to the cells of the sensitive tissues—to those of the epidermis in the case of an urticaria, to those of the naso-pharyngeal epithelium in the case of a hayfever or other specific rhinitis, and to those of the epithelium and the plain muscle coats of the bronchioles, in the case of a specific, allergic asthma. Obviously such a naturally acquired condition is closely related to, if not identical with, some kinds, at least of artificially produced anaphylaxis. And the part played in the production of the characteristic symptoms, by the release of histamine when the antigen makes contact with the allergic cells, is made clear, not only by the nature of the symptoms themselves, but by the successful suppression of these symptoms, in many cases, by remedies of the growing class of the "antihistamines," the development of which had its beginning with the researches made during the War and the Occupation, here, in Paris, by Dr. Halpern and Dr. Bovet, and now being so eagerly pursued all over the world.

We may feel certain that all such advances of knowledge, with regard to related conditions, will promote a more complete understanding of the condition of anaphylaxis, as produced under the now classical, experimental conditions. And we may be glad, I think, to recognize that progress is so well advanced towards a complete understanding of the phenomenon of anaphylaxis, as we celebrate this fiftieth anniversary of its discovery.

15

TRANSMISSION OF EFFECTS
FROM NERVE-ENDINGS*

A SURVEY OF THE SIGNIFICANCE OF PRESENT KNOWLEDGE

THE LAST eighty years or so have seen an almost continuous study by physiologists of the wave of excitation, or impulse —the phenomenon which the late Keith Lucas called "the propagated disturbance"—as it is conducted within the limits of an excitable nerve- or muscle-fibre. Starting from an excited point on such a fibre, the propagated wave sweeps along it at a uniform high speed, and equally in both directions; and, in the nerve-fibre, a momentary change in the electrical potential at the surface membrane of the fibre is the only sign of its passage. In years still recent, in which electronic amplifying and recording instruments have made experiments possible on single nerve-fibres, including some on the very large fibres which occur in the nerves of certain cephalopods, a rapid advance has taken place in knowledge of the meaning of this change in polarization at the fibre surface, which accompanies the excitatory state. It is this change which, by initiating a closure of local electrical circuits in rapid succession, causes the process of excitation to be conducted thus swiftly along the whole length of the fibre, by an essentially electrical process. In the normal, resting fibre, nerve or muscle, the surface potential is such that the outside is electrically positive to the inside of the fibre; and the data now available show that excitation, when it rises to the level at which the swiftly propagated impulse is started, causes not merely, as was formerly supposed, a reduction, or negative variation, of this resting polarization, but an actual reversal; so that the outside of the fibre becomes, for the moment, electronegative to the inside. And we are getting now so near to the fundamentals in the understanding of this process, through the work of Hodgkin, Huxley, and Katz, and of many others, that it is possible already to express this change of polarization in terms of a change in the

---

* Final Open Post-Graduate Lecture of the Candlemas Term 1952 at the University of St. Andrews Medical School. Delivered at Dundee on 13th March, 1952.

surface membrane, such as to cause a flow of sodium ions from the external medium to the interior of the fibre, and a smaller flow of potassium ions from the inside to the outside. But the physico-chemical structure of the membrane which causes this polarizing ionic separation at rest, the means of its maintenance, the mode of its breakdown with excitation, the process of its restoration when the excitation has passed—these, I suppose, are still the ultimate physiological mysteries.

So much for the impulse conducted within the limits of a single excitable cell. If physiology is ever thus to be able to interpret vital processes in terms of simpler, physico-chemical changes, it is probably necessary thus to simplify the problem, by the isolation of single vital units for study. But the living organism is not a mere heap of similar cells, a mere fabric of similar fibres, or a mere congeries of similar vital units; and we must avoid the temptation too readily to assume that such a conduction process must be continuous, even when excitation appears to pass, with only a brief delay, from one such cell or fibre unit to another, at points where they make intimate contact with one another.

Until relatively recent years, however, the assumption of such continuity was common among physiologists; and, indeed, when it was found that a nerve impulse, reaching an inter-neuronal synapse or a motor nerve-ending on a muscle-fibre, reappeared with only a brief delay on the other side of the junction, as a similarly conducted wave of excitation in the secondary nerve axon or muscle-fibre, it was natural to suppose that the excitation had, indeed, been conducted across the synaptic or neuromuscular contact by an essentially identical, electrical process. And there are, I believe, still some physiologists of experience and authority who have not yet freed themselves from the lure of this uniform interpretation. It would have been the natural and proper one, indeed, if there had been no evidence to indicate that the transmission of the excitation across such junctions had characters of its own, and to suggest that something must happen there which was different in its nature and not merely in its time relations, from the swift conduction within the limits of a nerve-fibre or a muscle-fibre. These special characters, indeed, are by no means all matters of recent discovery. Many have been known since the middle years of the nineteenth century, and some even longer than that. Let us glance at them in rapid survey.

1. The first and most general of the characters distinguishing this transmission of excitation, across such junctions between nerve-fibre endings and other neurones or "effector" cells, is that it is strictly unidirectional; the transmission is effective only from nerve-fibre ending to responsive cell and never in the reverse direction; whereas within the limits of a nerve- or muscle-fibre, as we have seen, it goes equally well in both directions. And note that if the excitation were transmitted across the junction by eddy current action, by the formation of electrical circuits creating new relative cathodes, we should expect it to go most easily, perhaps only indeed, from the large muscle-fibre to the slender nerve-ending. In fact, when an artificial contact is made between nerve and muscle, as in the old experiment of the rheosopic frog, the excitation can be seen to be electrically transmitted from the muscle to the nerve, and never from the nerve to the muscle. Yet it is in that other direction, from the tiny nerve-ending to the bulky muscle-fibre, that the excitation is always transmitted in their natural relations. Why, we may ask, if it is electrically transmitted, does it never go the other way? Why, when an electrically conducted impulse is sent along a muscle-fibre by stimulating it at one end, does it not stimulate the nerve-ending as it passes the point of contact, and send an impulse in the unnatural, antidromic direction up the nerve-fibre? Teleologically we find the answer readily enough. If such a two-way transport of excitation were possible at neuro-muscular contact-junctions, or at interneuronal synapses, the almost unimaginably complex but perfectly ordered traffic of nerve impulses, by which the whole body's functions are so exquisitely combined, attuned, and organized, would break down into a shimmering disarray, as ineffective, for purposes of the living and conscious organism, as that of a stricken heart, in which fibrillation has replaced the orderly succession of systole and diastole. On the once prevalent theory of a continuity of electrical conduction across the neuromuscular junctions, however, it was always necessary to make subsidiary and elaborate assumptions in order to explain the avoidance of such a chaos.

2. Since Claude Bernard worked and taught, it has been known that when the muscle fails to respond to stimulation of

its nerve, by reason of fatigue, or after the administration of curare, it is at the nerve-muscle junction that the failure occurs, the nerve alone, or the muscle alone, being both still capable of the normal conduction of an impulse. Langley showed that the stimulation and subsequent paralysis caused by nicotine was located at the synapses in a ganglion, the nerve-fibres on either side of them being unaffected. And, later, he and others showed that the effects of both nicotine and curarine, with quantitative differences only, are effective at ganglionic synapses and at nerve-muscle junctions in doses which do not affect conduction in the nerve-fibres. And now it can be stated, more definitely, that all the actions of these alkaloids at these junctions are on the ganglion cells and the motor end-plates, and not on the synaptic nerve-endings; so that these receptive cell-structures have a special chemical sensitiveness, and have it in common.

3. When we come to the involuntary, autonomic nervous system, and the transmission of the effects of impulses in its nerve-fibres to the involuntary muscle-coats of the viscera and similar structures, the necessity for considering some process other than simple, continuous conduction from nerve to muscle by an electrical mechanism, has long been obvious. For these involuntary muscle structures are automatically active, showing spontaneous tone and rhythm in the absence of any nervous stimulation; and when nerve impulses reach them along nerves from one or the other part of the autonomic system, the effects are in one or the other direction—of either augmentation or inhibition of the spontaneous tonic or rhythmic activity; the effects, on any one organ, of impulses from its sympathetic and from its parasympathetic nerve-supply, being commonly in opposite directions, increase and decrease respectively of its tone and rhythm. Thus the parasympathetic vagus inhibits the activity of the heart and augments that of the gastro-intestinal canal, while the sympathetic nerves to these same structures have the opposite effects in both cases, augmenting the rhythmic activity of the heart and inhibiting the tone and rhythm of the stomach and the bowel.

There are, of course, many other such cases; and it was clearly difficult, in any of them, to postulate a mechanism which would enable the same kind of nerve impulses, conducted along nerve-fibres often having different anatomical origins, indeed, but otherwise indistinguishable, to change the activity of an effector organ in opposite senses, if they were transmitted to it by a simple continuation of the same electrical process as that responsible for their conduction along the nerves. Something of a different *kind* must surely happen at the endings of these autonomic nerve-fibres on the involuntary muscle-cells.

That was the state of this problem of synaptic or neuro-muscular transmission right up to the end of the nineteenth century. Then it was still just a problem waiting for solution. It is not my purpose to-day to attempt anything like a detailed review of the experimental advances in knowledge in the past half-century, which have made it possible, on this formerly confused and largely vacant background, to begin to trace the outlines, at least, of a coherent picture. A hint towards its construction might, indeed, have been earlier derived from some of the evidence which I have already mentioned. We have seen that there was evidence of a specific chemical sensitiveness to certain poisons, shown by something located in the junctions of nerve-endings and responsive cells, which we now know to be the receptive cells, or specially receptive parts of these, not the incident nerve-endings. And it was natural that the first steps towards a clearer understanding should come from studies of the autonomic nervous system, and of the reactions of the involuntary muscle and gland cells of the different organs controlled by its impulses, first to certain vegetable poisons, and then to powerfully active bases natural to the body. As long ago as the 1860's the work of Schmiedeberg and his colleagues had shown that the actions of the toadstool-alkaloid, muscarine, closely imitated the effects of impulses in the vagus nerve on the heart and other organs. To nobody, however, not even to a Gaskell, had this resemblance suggested anything but a natural anomaly. It was the discovery by Oliver and Schäfer of the intense activity of suprarenal extracts, and the recognition by Lewandowsky, by Langley and, with pure adrenaline, by Elliott, of the detailed resemblance of these actions, augmentor and inhibitor on different organs, to those of true sympathetic nerves, which opened a new chapter of the story. And it was Elliott's brilliant suggestion, of an actual liberation of minute doses of adrenaline at sympathetic nerve-endings, to act as the chemical, pharmacodynamic transmitter of their effects to the responsive cells, which furnished the clue to all that follows. Let us turn aside for a moment to note what experiments have added to that particular chapter, even in the past few years. As early as 1910 I had drawn attention to imperfections in the resemblance between the actions of adrenaline and those of impulses in sympathetic nerves; and I had even pointed out that the actions of its lower homologue, *nor*-adrenaline, reproduced the sympathetic effects with a closer fidelity. And now, some forty years later, there has been a veritable spate of evidence from v. Euler, Holtz, Gaddum, Burn, all of these former co-workers of mine, and from Professor Hunter, Dr. West and Dr. Shepherd, of this School, showing that the chemical transmitter of sympathetic effects—or, in the terminology which I later introduced to avoid the sometimes misleading anatomical implication, the transmitter of the effects of *adrenergic* nerves—is, indeed, predominantly *nor*-adrenaline, with adrenaline as only a minor component, in many animals. Dr. West and his co-workers have found that, in most of the animal species which they have examined, *nor*-adrenaline is especially predominant in the suprarenal glands of the foetus and the newly born. The current number of the *Journal of Physiology* contains a further note from this Medical School (Hunter, Shepherd, and West) showing that the curious para-aortic organs of Zuckerkandl, which degenerate and disappear in early childhood, contain, while they last, a remarkably high proportion of *nor*-adrenaline. That digression, however, has taken us far ahead of a proper chronological sequence.

To complete Elliott's conception, which, in the meantime, had, in fact, been almost forgotten, we required some chemical claimant more likely to be found in the animal body than muscarine, and much less persistent in its action, for the rôle of transmitter of the alternative range of autonomic effects, produced in general, but not always, by nerves of parasympathetic origin. And a suitable candidate came to light in 1914, almost by accident, in the acetic-ester of choline, acetylcholine, which had an intense action of the kind required, very quickly cut short by the destructive action of an esterase, now known to be a specific "cholinesterase." Acetylcholine was found to produce, indeed, the effects of parasympathetic or, to use again the later and more strictly accurate terminology, of "cholinergic" nerves, with a fidelity even closer than that with which those of sympathetic (adrenergic) nerves had been found to be produced by adrenaline; and, of course, for the like reason. For, as is now so well known, Otto Loewi, some seven years later, obtained direct evidence of the release in the frog's heart of transmitters indistinguishable from acetylcholine and adrenaline, when its vagus and its sympathetic nerves were respectively stimulated. My own experiments on acetylcholine, however, had shown that, in addition to its muscarine-like effects, it was a powerful stimulant of autonomic ganglion cells and also, though the adequate evidence for this was longer deferred, of the motor end-plates of voluntary muscles. But the suggestion raised by these other actions, of a possible intervention of acetyl-choline as a transmitter of the rapid, individualized excitations at ganglionic synapses and motor-nerve end-plate junctions, was a much more difficult one to entertain. Even my own co-workers and I were long deterred from putting it even to the test of direct experiment; but, when the force of analogy gave us at last the courage to do this, the evidence came quickly, and it appeared to us to be unequivocal.

Much of this phase of a general development, with all the resistance which it most naturally encountered from electro-physiological orthodoxy, is already passing into history, I suppose; and cholinergic transmission at these peripheral synapses appears now to have become an item of current teaching. For evidence of its acceptance, and of its development in far more beautiful detail than my associates and I had ever contem-plated, I would refer you to a paper by Dr. Fatt and Professor Katz in a recent number of the *Journal of Physiology*. Obtaining electrical records, with a micro-electrode, from a single motor end-plate of a frog's muscle-fibre, and recording the depolariza-tion of this end-plate, which follows the arrival of a nerve impulse at the motor nerve-ending in contact with its surface, these authors have been able to reach some truly remarkable conclusions. They calculate, for example, that an electrical effect involving the simultaneous release of the whole of the ions present in the motor nerve-ending would be required, to produce the depolarization observed at the end-plate surface; and they conclude that only a specific, pharmacodynamic effect, such as the acetylcholine released there by the arrival of an impulse at the nerve-ending could produce, would account for the effect observed. On the other hand, recording the effect of an impulse electrically propagated from a distant point on the muscle-fibre, as it passes the end-plate with its micro-electrode, they reach the conclusion, perhaps even more surprising, that the end-plate itself is incapable of responding to an electrical stimulus thus applied to it.*

And I suppose that we are entitled to assume that Professor Eccles, with whom Professor Katz had earlier collaborated, has now withdrawn the opposition which he had hitherto so stoutly maintained against our evidence for a similar cholin-ergic transmission of the excitatory process at the synapses in the autonomic ganglia—evidence which my colleagues and I had always regarded as more directly demonstrative, even than that for the analogous transmission from motor nerve-endings to muscle-fibres. For Professor Eccles now proclaims his conviction that transmission of the excitatory action across the countless synaptic junctions of the central nervous system is also effected by the release of chemical agents from the endings of the presynaptic fibres. We, who had so long been concerned with the evidence for such chemical transmission in the peri-pheral system, would still have regarded this as a tremendous extrapolation; and some of us, I think, had hardly expected to live long enough to see it experimentally justified. Professor Eccles's sudden conversion, however, is a direct result of his brilliant experimental success in introducing micro-electrodes into single motoneurones of the anterior horn of the cat's spinal cord; and it is an electric change recorded under these condi-tions which has convinced him that synaptic transmission to such central neurones requires also a chemical agent. His method enables him to record the difference of potential across the surface of such a cell at rest; and the inside is found to be electro-negative to the outside to the extent of some 70 millivolts. Then, when a reflex, excitatory impulse arrives at the synap-tic endings in contact with the cell surfaces, there is a swing of this negative potential back towards electrical neutrality, reminiscent of the end-plate potential of a muscle-fibre; and,

---

* Prof. Katz, in response to a recent enquiry, has been good enough to confirm this statement as representing the views of Dr. Fatt and himself concerning the most probable, though not the only possible, interpretation of their findings. He suggests, however, that "end-plate receptors" might more accurately give their meaning, since the whole end-plate region, a rather diffuse structure in a frog's muscle-fibre, may contain electrically excitable areas as well.

continuing the resemblance, if this primary swing rises above some 30 millivolts, it gives origin to a rapid spike-potential, large enough momentarily to reverse the polarization of the cell-membrane, and then to be propagated as an impulse out along the axone-fibre. On the other hand, if a reflex *inhibitory* impulse arrives at the synapse, its effect is to cause a slower wave of *increase* of the resting polarization, during which the depolarizing effect of an excitatory impulse arriving at the synapse, being partly balanced by the super-polarization, is ineffective in releasing a propagated spike-impulse. It is this inhibitory *increase* of the resting polarization of the cell-membrane which Eccles finds impossible to reconcile with any kind of theory of transmission by an electrical process. And, if the reflex *inhibition* can thus be explained, as he now supposes, only by the intervention of a chemical transmitter, Eccles concludes that the primary fall of the resting potential caused by a reflex *excitation*, with its suggestive resemblance to the end-plate potential in a muscle-fibre, must also be regarded as due to a chemical transmitter and, presumably, to a different one.

Thus we arrive at a conception of the transmission, by chemical agents yet unknown, of excitation and inhibition at central nervous synapses; and this again presents more than one suggestive analogy to the mechanism which has now long been accepted for the augmentor and inhibitor actions of the known transmitters of the effects of autonomic nerve impulses. There we have long known that the same transmitter, whether it be acetylcholine or adrenaline, may augment the activity of one organ and inhibit that of another. It must be noted that, in the monosynaptic reflexes, with which these recent observations by Eccles are concerned, it seems to be most unlikely that either of the already recognized transmitters is responsible for the effects; for the nerve-fibres of the dorsal roots and columns contain no significant amounts either of acetylcholine, or of adrenaline or its primary homologue. On the other hand, the studies by Feldberg and his co-workers of the distribution of acetylcholine, and of the enzymes which form and destroy it, especially of the cholinacetylase which can be recognized and estimated in very small samples of tissue, have created a strong presumption in favour of a cholinergic transmission at certain synaptic levels in the central nervous system; and they were able to cite cases in which the available evidence suggested that the neurones providing a certain tract of fibres were cholinergic, but that those with which these in turn make their synaptic endings had a different chemical transmitter function; just as, on the other hand, if we accept Eccles's conclusion, the non-cholinergic, sensory, dorsal-root fibres must use some other transmitters than acetylcholine, to effect transmission at their synaptic contacts with the undoubtedly cholinergic motoneurones of the anterior horn. And for a peripheral example of this kind of succession we may recall that the cholinergic fibres of the cervical sympathetic nerve form synapses with the adrenergic neurones of the superior cervical ganglion. Such an alternation of chemical functions, in successive neurones of a polysynaptic chain, can clearly occur; though, on the other hand, we can easily find examples of two cholinergic neurones in direct succession, as in the vagus innervation of the heart and other organs, or the innervation of the pupil by the third cranial nerve, where cholinergic preganglionic fibres make synaptic connections with the also cholinergic secondary neurones of the ciliary ganglion. In any case, if two possible kinds of transmission are available, cholinergic and otherwise, we need no elaborate statistics to predict that they will, in some instances, occur alternately, and that the probable frequency of such an alternation will increase with the number of neurones in a synaptic sequence.

If Professor Eccles is right, it would seem, then, that we may have to look for more than two transmitters—for at least two unknowns in addition to the known acetylcholine—to function at central synapses. And, if experience with the recognition of transmitters in the peripheral system goes for anything, those who undertake the quest may need some luck to bring to their notice the kind of substances which they might consider as likely candidates for these central synaptic functions. If Dr. Oliver had not persuaded Professor Schäfer, against his inclination, to try the effect of a suprarenal extract at the end of another experiment; if Dr. Reid Hunt had not chanced to observe the great enhancement of the depressor action of choline when his chemical colleague Dr. Taveau acetylated it for him; if I myself, some eight years later, had not encountered this acetylcholine as a constituent of an odd extract of ergot, and had not been incited thereby to make a systematic study of the remarkable range of its intense activities; if such accidents as these had not brought the two substances to notice, and led to the recognition of the close resemblances between their actions and the effects produced by the nerves of certain systems—then it seems to me that, if the idea of a chemical transmission of nervous effects had been seriously considered at all, we might still be wondering what sort of substances we ought to look for as possible candidates for these transmitter functions. When once we knew what substances to look for, it was not so difficult to find them, and, when Loewi's pioneer demonstration had shown the way, to detect their release from the different types of nerve-endings when impulses arrived there. But where shall we start in the central nervous system?

There is one observation, made in connexion with the study of chemical transmission in the peripheral system, which might possibly furnish a clue. The transmitter used by nerve-fibres of a particular kind, and concentrated at their endings in readiness for release, is also to be found along the whole length of the fibres; a transmitter is characteristic, then, not only of the endings, but of the whole neurones. We have seen how Feldberg and Vogt have been able to use this fact. Somebody, perhaps, may yet be able to obtain by extraction from the fibres of the dorsal roots, and then to identify, a substance with physiological activities which might justify a consideration of it as a possible transmitter of monosynaptic reflex effects to moto-neurones. What shall we expect of such a substance? The synaptic endings in the central system represent only one end of these dorsal-root fibres. Are we to expect that the transmitter at their central, synaptic endings would also be functional at their peripheral endings, and possibly be there concerned with transmitting the so-called antidromic vasodilator action? We have clearly no right to assume it; on the other hand, there is no justification for regarding as impossible, *a priori*, the possession by a single substance of two transmitter actions apparently so unrelated. For we have long known of such a double function in the case of acetylcholine, which has an intense inhibitor action on the tone of all systemic arterioles and, on the other hand, a stimulating action on ganglion cells

and muscle end-plates, which enables it to act as the transmitter
to those structures of the excitatory effects of impulses reaching
the synaptic endings of preganglionic and motor nerve-fibres.
Nor do we lack an analogy for the possibility that impulses in a
single sensory fibre, branching in the spiral cord to make synapses
with an extensor and a flexor motoneurone, and releasing the same
transmitter at both these endings, might use it to excite activity
in the one case and to inhibit it in the other. For we are reminded
again of the known peripheral transmitters, acetylcholine and
adrenaline, either of which can augment the activity of plain
muscle in one viscus and inhibit it in the plain muscle of another.
Nor is there lack of analogy for the positive variation of the
resting membrane potential which accompanies, and apparently accounts for, the synaptic inhibition of a spinal motoneurone. We can find a good parallel for it in the positive
variation produced by vagus stimulation in the resting potential
of the tortoise auricle, as demonstrated by the late W. H. Gaskell
in 1887—sixty-five years ago!

The only difference which more recent studies have made
in our interpretation of this long-known electrical concomitant of the vagus inhibition of heart muscle, is that we should
now confidently attribute it to the release of acetylcholine,
in contact with the muscle-fibres. Let us be on our guard,
however, against too easy an assumption that this finally disposes
of the problem. We have become accustomed now to attribute the opposite effects, on different effector organs, of impulses of the same kind in nerve-fibres of the same origin, to
the similarly contrasted effects on the same structures of a transmitter substance. When we observe, for example, that parasympathetic impulses cause contraction of the bladder fundus
and inhibition of its sphincter, we attribute this, and rightly,
to the fact that acetylcholine, which they liberate, has the same
contrasted effects. And we may be in danger of imagining
that the question is thereby settled, the ultimate problem solved.
And if Professor Eccles rightly interprets his observations of
potential changes in single motoneurones, the same tendency
may presently arise, in considering excitation and inhibition at
central synapses; there, also, we may be tempted to suppose
that the problem presented by the excitation of one neurone
and the inhibition of another, by impulses impinging upon

them from two branches of a single fibre, will be solved by the discovery of one transmitter, producing both of these contrasted effects. Let me, therefore, suggest to you that such discoveries do not solve, or even begin to solve the real problem; they merely define it. They make it clear, indeed, that the question is no longer why a plain muscle-fibre, or a nerve-cell, is stimulated or inhibited by the same kind of electrical eddy current; they leave untouched the question why it reacts in this way or that to sudden contact with one chemical substance. The ultimate problem may thus, at the next stage, be approached by the methods of Pharmacology rather than by those of Electrophysiology; but this does not exclude the possibility that the pharmacological attack may itself reach a point at which a study of effects at a membrane, by electrical methods, will offer in turn the only opening to yet further progress.

Meanwhile, however, the recognition of the intervention of a chemical, pharmacodynamic phase, in the transmission of the excitatory process at one-way junctions, has already shown the way to new and more detailed interpretations of the actions of various alkaloids and pathological products, and to more rational therapeutic interventions. We already know a great deal more, for example, about the actions of physostigmine (eserine) and substances of analogous action, and about those of atropine and the curares. Knowledge of the mode of action of the latter, together with the isolation and availability of a pure, crystalline curarine, have converted this drug, from a laboratory curiosity and an occasional tool of experiment, into a valuable and trusted aid to the anaesthetist and the surgeon. Various curare substitutes are coming into view and into use; and we can distinguish those among them which, like curarine, protect the motor end-plates from the depolarizing action of the acetylcholine released at motor nerve-endings, from others which also render them insensitive to acetylcholine, but by the opposite method of inducing a persistent depolarization, at and beyond the end-plate surface. Others again, rendering ganglion cells insensitive to acetylcholine released at synapses, produce a vaso-motor weakening and thus a low arterial pressure which, with appropriate postural adjustments, is being widely used now for the production of bloodless fields of operation. On the other hand, knowledge of the chemical transmitter function is furnishing clues, at least, to the nature of the different defects produced by the toxins of tetanus and botulism, and of that occurring naturally in *myasthenia gravis*; and, in the latter case, it is pointing the way to treatment which, though it be symptomatic only, is both rationally based and effective. So that, even if the recognition of the chemical phase in transmission only redefines the nature of the problem, shifting it a further stage towards its ultimate solution, it is yielding crops, meanwhile, of knowledge applicable in practical medicine; and who can predict what the harvest may be, if, from the beginnings already made, progress continues in the establishment of its application to the seemingly infinite complexities of the central nervous synapses?